A CREATIVE STEP-BY-STEP GUIDE

PROPAGATION

A CREATIVE STEP-BY-STEP GUIDE

PROPAGATION

Author
Peter Blackburne-Maze

Photographer
Neil Sutherland

COOMBE BOOKS

4664 Propagation: A Creative Step-by-Step Guide
This edition published in 1999 by Coombe Books
© 1999 Quadrillion Publishing Limited,
Godalming, Surrey, GU7 1XW, UK
Printed and bound in Italy
All rights reserved
ISBN 1-84100-223-2

Credits
Edited, designed and typeset: Ideas into Print
American Consultant: Catriona Tudor Erler
Photographs: Neil Sutherland
For Quadrillion: Jane Alexander, Sandra Dixon

The publishers would like to thank Robinsons Greenhouses
of Millbrook, Southampton, UK, for supplying a
greenhouse for photographic purposes.

THE AUTHOR

Peter Blackburne-Maze has spent his whole working life in
horticulture. He started with growing fruit commercially,
but soon widened his experience to take in most aspects
of horticulture. Following 11 years experience in the
agrochemical industry, he has for the past 20 years, been a
horticultural consultant and writer. He is a regular
contributor to a number of gardening magazines covering
ornamentals, fruit and vegetables. He is the past Chairman
of the RHS Fruit Group and a member of the RHS Fruit
and Vegetable Committee.

THE PHOTOGRAPHER

Neil Sutherland has more than 30 years experience in a
wide range of photographic fields, including still-life,
portraiture, reportage, natural history, cookery, landscape
and travel. His work has been published in countless books
and magazines throughout the world.

*Half-title page: The seeds of runner bean 'Painted Lady'.
Like other members of the large family of peas and beans,
these are easy to sow for a fresh crop each season.*

*Title page: You can raise many garden plants from seeds
or cuttings, such as these pelargoniums, impatiens and
begonias, using the simplest equipment.*

*Copyright page: Lilium 'Enchantment'. An excellent hybrid
suitable for growing in pots and borders. Propagate by
separating and replanting the bulb scales in spring.*

CONTENTS

Part One

ESSENTIAL TECHNIQUES

There is usually more to plant propagation than meets the eye, which is why it is such a fascinating branch of gardening. First of all, though, why propagate plants at all? They are easy to buy from most garden centers or even specialist nurseries if you are having difficulties finding the specific plants you want. The main reason is probably cost. Most of us are reluctant to spend money on buying something when, for a very modest outlay, we could produce it ourselves. Then there is the sense of achievement. Even the most experienced gardener loves to create something new. Finally, it is sometimes a matter of necessity. There may be a particular plant you have always wanted, but have never been able to buy. Then you see it in someone else's garden and it is the work of a moment to slip up to the front door and ask for a cutting.

In the first part of this book we consider how plants reproduce naturally, because here you will find valuable clues to help you decide how to propagate them yourself. The simplest and most productive method is sowing seeds, but this soon leads to other things. Success with the simpler methods of propagation, such as layering, division and cuttings, will encourage you to attempt some of the more elaborate techniques. The emphasis here is always on the easiest ways of propagating a particular plant. These are not necessarily the most productive methods in terms of numbers produced, but they are comparatively simple to follow and almost always successful. Where there is more than one way of propagating a plant, we describe the easier method first. The most important aspect of plant propagation is attention to detail. Conditions have to be right if results are to be good. Above all, plant propagation should be enjoyable, even fun. Then you will succeed.

Left: Crocus tommasinianus.   **Right:** *Poppy in bud, flower and seedpod.*

Right: Dandelions provide us with the perfect example of how Nature disperses seeds – in this case, to the four winds. Each seed has its own parachute that carries it away by catching every breath of wind.

Left: Acorns are the seeds of the oak tree. They form in cups and when ripe, these heavy seeds simply fall to the ground. They are not thrown any distance from the parent plant.

The runner bean makes little effort to disperse its seeds. Its cultivation by man ensures a wide distribution!

Many grass seeds, including these from hare's tail, have slightly hairy coats or even minute hooks that catch in the fleece, hair or wool of passing animals which carry the seeds far and wide.

Sempervivum seed is very small and produced in large quantities. Tiny seed is less likely to survive, so more is needed.

Birds help to disperse many seeds, such as these from sunflowers. As the birds feed, seeds fall down cracks in the ground and germinate.

One very important thing to remember about propagation is that Nature has done it all before, otherwise there would be no plants around today. In many cases, we can improve on the technique employed in the wild. The first and most obvious way in which plants spread themselves is by seed. It is also the most productive method. Interestingly, seed is the only method that involves the sexual parts of the plants, i.e. the flowers, which produce seeds after pollination and fertilization. All other forms of plant propagation are asexual, or vegetative. Layering is probably Nature's most widely used vegetative system; it is always cropping up in the wild. Where part of a plant, such as the shoots or shoot tips, touch the ground, roots form and soon another self-contained plant appears. Oddly enough, the most commonly used vegetative method of propagation – taking cuttings – is almost unheard of in nature, but suckers from the roots of certain plants (plum and cherry) and plantlets on the end of stolons (strawberries and ajuga) are commonplace. Grafting is another example. How often have we seen two branches of the same tree or bush, or even neighbouring ones, fused together where they have been in contact for years? That is an example of Nature grafting. And budding and grafting are used by nurserymen to grow new ornamental trees and shrubs and fruit trees.

Right: This large Ginkgo biloba seed has germinated and is growing away strongly. The root appears before the shoot so that the developing plant is supported before it starts to grow tall.

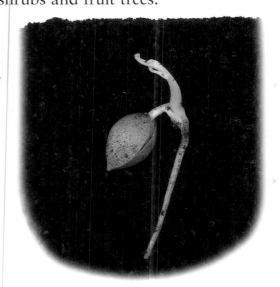

Above: *As well as producing seeds in their fruits, strawberries also spread by means of plantlets that develop at the end of above-ground stolons, or runners. It is these plantlets that we use to propagate strawberries.*

Right: *Ajuga (bugleweed) also spreads by producing plantlets at the end of above-ground stolons. Its plantlets are produced closer to the parent than in strawberries and it is more productive.*

Above: *Sempervivum uses plantlets at the end of stolons to reproduce, as well as seeds. Employing two totally different reproductive strategies is a safe way of increasing your own kind.*

Ferns

Ferns are a fascinating and extremely ancient group of plants. Along with mare's tail (equisetum), liverwort and mosses, they are amongst the oldest plants on Earth. One reason for their survival, as well as their local hardiness, is that they have developed systems of reproduction that have stood the test of time. In some cases, a single species has more than one way of reproducing. For example, bracken, mostly spreads by underground and overground rhizomes, but it also produces spores. Others develop plantlets on the edge or along the middle of their mature leaves. When these reach a certain size, they drop off the leaf, strike root and grow into another fern plant.

However, the majority of ferns reproduce by spores. Think of these as fern "seeds," but with a difference. Seeds drop out of, say, a seed capsule, fall to the ground and, in the right conditions, germinate and grow into a new plant. With fern spores, the system is more complicated. These are released with force from the sporangia, a fern's equivalent to a seedhead. Being like dust, they are blown about and eventually fall to the ground. Those that land in a suitable place will germinate. However, instead of growing into little fern plants, they form what is called a prothallus, an intermediate stage between spore and fern. Once the prothallus reaches a certain size, it produces a male and a female part, in much the same way as a flower does. The female part stays as part of the prothallus whereas the male is mobile, as is pollen. When the two meet, fertilization takes place and eventually the prothallus produces a tiny fern plant.

Left: *Ferns have carried the numbers game to the most amazing lengths. By producing millions of spores, they have ensured that they will not die out. Even if only two or three succeed in becoming adult plants, the parent has done its job.*

Below: *Some ferns produce plantlets along the leaf midrib towards mid-summer. These drop off and root under the parent plant. Some ferns produce both plantlets and spores.*

Nature has provided raspberries with even more than belt and suspenders. The large buds at the base of the stem give rise to new canes that will flower and fruit in their second year, thus providing seeds for dispersal.

The bumps on the upper surface of this raspberry root are adventitious buds that will develop into new canes.

Above: This new raspberry shoot could be from a bud on the base of a cane or, more likely, from a root bud.

Below: Like other bearded irises, Iris 'Jane Phillips' multiplies by branching rhizomes. After flowering or in early fall, dig up a clump, cut off suitable terminal pieces and replant them.

Above: Many irises, such as this Iris pumila, *multiply by producing two new rhizomes at the end of each existing one during the growing season.*

Above: The underground stolons of this mini-bamboo have needle-sharp tips that force their way through the ground to establish fresh clumps.

Roots are forming at every node along this horizontal ivy shoot.

Right: Hedera helix 'Ceridwen' is an attractive ivy cultivar and can be propagated by making use of ivy's ability to produce roots wherever a shoot lies in contact with the soil.

Left: Ivy can produce roots from any point on their shoots. If the shoots are running along the ground, the roots are terrestrial and will grow into the soil. If the stem is vertical, it will send out aerial roots to hang onto anything it can for support.

Bulbs and corms

Botanically, bulbs and corms are just modified underground stems. The main bulk of a bulb is made up of compressed, overlapping and grossly swollen leaves. Right at the bottom is the basal plate – the true stem. A tulip bulb is structurally much

the same as a daffodil bulb, but because the true leaves are quite dissimilar, so is the appearance of the bulb. Here, the true leaves are much broader, so the bulb also consists of broader, larger but fewer leaves. A corm is an almost entirely compressed and swollen stem, with dried and vestigial leaves on the outside. You will find small buds under the dried leaves on the surface. This replicates the structure of a vegetative shoot, i.e. a stem in the center and leaves on the outside with buds at their base.

Left: More than any other flower, the daffodil – here 'Dutch Master' – heralds spring and a new growing season. Apply a fertilizer after flowering to help the plants swell the new bulbs that produce the following spring's flowers.

The basic daffodil bulb is a single structure with roots and a flower embryo deep in the center.

At the end of the growing season, three small bulbs have developed. They will not flower until they are large enough.

The developing bulbs are clearly visible from the outside.

This cross-section shows secondary smaller bulbs attached to the main one. These bulbs will become more defined as they grow.

Helping Nature along

Some of the propagation methods that we employ are not quite as foolproof as we might think or wish, and it is sometimes necessary to bring in something to make the job more successful. The simplest example is probably putting a pot of soft cuttings in a plastic bag to stop them drying out. This in itself is improving the chances of the cuttings forming roots. In fact, nearly all the gadgets and tricks that we use are aimed at reducing the time between starting the process and finishing up with a self-sufficient plant. You might even call these aids to propagation "improvements on Nature." However, there is sometimes a temptation to go too far – to a point when the gadgets require more high-tech knowledge and experience than the horticultural side itself. This is merely putting gardening down as one of the many uses of technology. Gadgets should be a means to an end, not the end itself.

The non-electric propagator is probably the most valuable aid to propagation. It keeps your cuttings and seeds warm and moist at minimal cost. This in turn keeps the plant material alive for longer, so that its chance of rooting is increased.

Hormone rooting powder helps the cut on the base of the cutting to form a callus from which new roots will grow.

Use a pencil or stick to make holes in the potting mixture for cuttings.

Modern potting mixtures provide perfect drainage with good water retention. This allows oxygen (in the air) to reach the buried parts of propagation material and, at the same time, to keep it in a moist environment so that it remains alive long enough for roots to form.

A half-pot uses less potting mix than full-depth ones. The cuttings' roots will have plenty of room before they are planted up.

A mixture of moss peat and sharp sand is a cheap and effective rooting mixture. Moss peat holds plenty of moisture, but is an airy material that will allow oxygen to reach the roots.

Use sharp sand for good drainage.

Plastic bags are excellent in place of propagators but naturally have a more limited use. They are good for single pots of cuttings. Place the pot in a bag and tie up the neck to prevent the potting mixture drying out.

An electric propagator has all the benefits of non-electric (unheated) models, but includes a source of heat that keeps the cuttings or seeds warm. This encourages them to root sooner. Both models are used for germinating seeds in pots and do away with the need to heat whole greenhouses.

Most of the time you will be sowing seeds or inserting cuttings into pots or half-pots. Usually, half-pots are better because you seldom need a greater depth of potting mixture. Transfer seedlings or rooted cuttings into individual pots soon after they start growing.

Vermiculite has much the same uses as sharp sand but with the advantage of being much lighter. Additionally, it holds a great deal of water and can be used on its own for rooting cuttings. Always choose the horticultural product, not the one used in the building trade.

Hormone rooting powder or liquid can be used with most cuttings, but the late-summer, semi-ripe ones benefit most. The powder has a very short active life in the tub, so renew it every year to be on the safe side.

Sharp, or gritty sand mixed in equal parts with peat or peat substitute provides a well-drained but water-retentive rooting mixture. You can also add it to the surface of the mixture before inserting cuttings or sowing seed to stop the surface lying wet, which could lead to fungus diseases.

Labels are essential but frequently forgotten. This may seem trivial, but when you have spent valuable time sowing or taking cuttings, it is very annoying, some weeks later, to have pots full of plants and no idea what they are.

Making a heated propagator

The main advantage of a heated propagator is that it provides the right conditions for germinating seeds and striking cuttings – the two most widely used methods of plant propagation. It also avoids the need to create these conditions in a whole greenhouse or even indoors, if you have no greenhouse. And if only the propagator needs to be heated, you can save on energy costs. In the simple propagator featured here, heating is provided by an undersoil electrical cable that heats the planting medium, as well as the air in the propagator. Once you are able to create a favorable environment, it follows that plants can be propagated outside the normal season. Seeds can be sown in early spring or even late winter, so that plants are ready for planting out earlier. Once the propagator is set up and running, it can be used either for housing pots of seeds or cuttings, or cuttings can be rooted straight into the potting mixture in the propagator. A propagator is not without its responsibilities. The first one is temperature control. A thermostat will operate the heating cable, but a very high temperature can build up in a propagator that is standing in sunshine with the top on. Watering is another priority. It is vital that you water a propagator frequently during sunny weather, be it in summer or winter.

Above: On a small scale, a bell-jar makes an ideal propagator. It is a bright airy covering for cuttings or seeds and prevents them drying out.

Using a propagator

You can buy propagators in a range of shapes and sizes, and if you make your own it can be larger or smaller than the one shown here; just apply the same principles. All the components are quite easy to obtain.

Bear in mind that a propagator is an aid to plant propagation, not to growing plants. When the seeds have sprouted or cuttings have rooted, prepare them for the outside world by growing them progressively cooler. If not, they will become weak and drawn.

Once set up, a heated propagator should need very little maintenance to keep it working efficiently. However, it is a good idea to renew the potting mixture or sand once a year to prevent a build up of nutrient salts and to reduce the risk of fungal diseases getting in. You can also give the wood a new coat of preservative then.

1 *Start by determining the size of the propagator and cut the wood accordingly. A base made from a sheet of coarse-grade particleboard provides a strong foundation.*

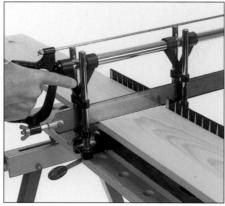

2 *Using a miter saw, cut the sides of the propagator absolutely square so that they butt together accurately. This gives a firmer and neater job in the long run.*

3 *Once all the pieces have been cut accurately, drill pilot holes and screw the four sides together. Brass or alloy screws are best because they resist rust and corrosion.*

4 *With the sides assembled, screw the base into place using rustproof screws. For added strength, apply a wood glue in the joints. Plane off any slight overlaps as necessary.*

Different substrates

We have used sand in this propagator because it is the easiest and cheapest material. However, if the propagator is larger or if it is going to be placed on a somewhat weak bench, then consider using a lighter material. Damp sand is extremely heavy, whereas damp perlite or horticultural vermiculite, even when wet, are still very light. They would also be marginally better if the propagator is used mainly for the direct rooting of cuttings.

5 Paint the inside and outside surfaces with a plant-friendly wood preservative, such as this green horticultural stain. Do not use pressure-treated timber.

6 When the preservative is dry, add a layer of sand about 1in deep. The heating cable will lie on this. Make sure the sand is level and firm it down so the cable will lie flat.

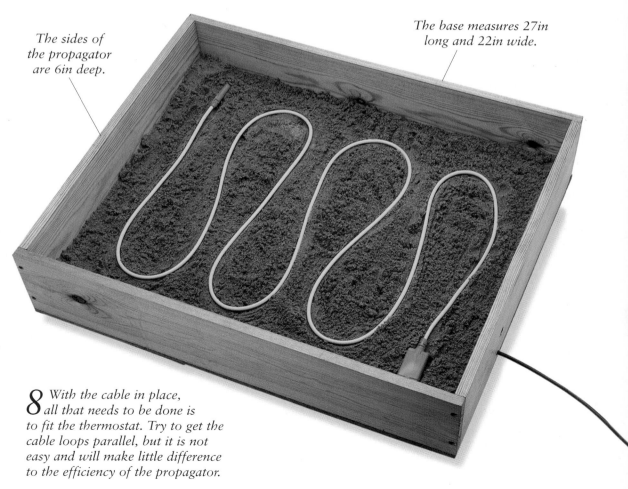

The sides of the propagator are 6in deep.

The base measures 27in long and 22in wide.

7 Snake the soil-warming cable back and forth across the sand base. You can buy a purpose-made cable complete with a thermostat and detailed fitting instructions.

8 With the cable in place, all that needs to be done is to fit the thermostat. Try to get the cable loops parallel, but it is not easy and will make little difference to the efficiency of the propagator.

19

9 Drill a hole in the side of the propagator so you can push through the rod of the thermostat. Suspend the rod above the cables, so that it crosses but does not touch them.

10 Be sure to install the rod correctly, otherwise you may get false readings that will either switch off the current too soon or leave it on too long. Cover the rod with a layer of sand.

Making the propagator lid

1 Make the lid from a sheet of twin-walled, translucent plastic. Start by cutting out a square at each corner of the sheet. It is light and easy to work with.

2 Score along the edges and fold up the sides to make a box shape about 8in deep. This should be ideal for normal use.

3 Join the edges with "green-house tape" which is thicker, wider and stickier than regular tape and contains a UV inhibitor.

4 Make the lid slightly smaller than the base so that it fits inside. Being translucent, the plastic provides some shade and its double skin acts as an insulator to retain warmth.

Temperature control

The thermostat rod buried in the sand detects the temperature of the sand and switches the electricity off or on to maintain a particular heat level in the propagator. Turn the dial to the temperature you need.

Above: *Simply turn the knob on the control box to the right setting. A reading of about 60°F will be fine for most purposes.*

Left: *With the cable and thermostat rod about 1.5-2in deep, there is room for cuttings without them coming into contact with the heating cables. The deeper the sand layer, the longer it will stay warm.*

Small seeds, such as lobelia and begonia, need warmth and moisture to germinate quickly and grow into strong seedlings. The propagator provides both of these. A further benefit is that the seedlings are less likely to damp off. Place some paper over the pot of seeds to reduce the light intensity and, therefore, the heat.

Sedum leaf cuttings are fairly long-lived, but a propagator creates the conditions they like best, with the result that they root quickly.

Pelargonium and other soft cuttings. Tip cuttings, which are naturally soft and tender, root quickest when they are small; they also die more quickly. Because they stand a better chance of surviving in a propagator than in the open air, you can use smaller cuttings for quicker results.

The normal way of propagating strawberries is to root the plantlets on the ends of the runners during or after fruiting by pegging them down when they are reasonable advanced. A propagator allows you to use much smaller plantlets much sooner.

These lavender cuttings are being rooted in the potting mixture that fills the base of the propagator. This has no particular propagation benefit except that it allows you to fit in more material, in this case between the pots and trays.

21

Pretreating seeds

Germinating seeds is not necessarily as straightforward as it seems. For example, many alpines and primulas, along with most meconopsis (Himalayan and Welsh poppies), need a period of intense cold and dark so that the seeds do not germinate too soon, only to be frozen during the winter. However, gorse seeds (ulex) must be subjected to fire before they will grow. In the wild, the burning is a trigger to get the seeds going. Some seeds will only germinate in the light, whereas others need to be kept in the dark. Between these two extremes are many other apparent idiosyncrasies. Fruits and berries, which are simply seed capsules, usually have to pass through a bird or animal before the seeds within will break into growth. (It is true that this is partly a distribution technique so that the seeds are spread far and wide, but the fleshy exterior must be discarded before the seeds will germinate.) Because warmth is a prerequisite of germination, many gardeners use a propagator or greenhouse to germinate seeds in the early spring. In most cases, the treatment that occurs naturally or that we administer will break down a growth-inhibiting hormone within the seed coat that is preventing germination. Dispersing the hormone allows the seeds to germinate. Once the seedcoat has been slightly damaged, moisture can enter and the seed begins to germinate.

Above: Sweet pea seeds sown in mid- to late autumn will give you earlier flowers the following summer. Over-winter young plants in a cold frame.

Preparing sweet peas

Soaking seeds in water overnight softens the seedcoat, but do not soak them any longer, as this can inhibit germination.

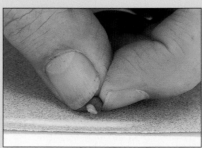

Left: By morning, most seeds will have swollen. If any have not done so, chip away a fragment of the outer coat with a sharp knife to allow moisture to get in.

Left: Rubbing the seedcoat on sandpaper is another strategy, but take care not to damage the underlying tissue. Avoid wounding the seed embryo.

Above: Be sure to check seeds sown in a propagator every day until germination occurs. Remove the lid for good air circulation and accustom the seedlings to cooler conditions.

Preparing berries

Many seeds form within berries or even large fruits. Often, the flesh of berries contains a germination-inhibiting hormone. To encourage the seeds inside to germinate in spring, you will need to break up the flesh and store the seeds cold during the winter.

Mountain ash, or rowan, berries

Special needs

Alstroemeria: Sow 0.25in deep and keep at 70°F for three to four days. Move to refrigerator for three weeks. Put back in the warmth.

Canna: File through seed coat to reach the white underneath. Soak for one to two days. Sow and keep at 70-75°F.

Cyclamen: Soak the seeds in warm water for a day before sowing to wash away growth inhibitor. Sow very shallowly and cover with aluminum foil or black plastic. Germinate at 61-68°F.

Lupin: Sandpaper the hard seed coat before sowing.

1 *With berries such as these from mountain ash (Sorbus aucuparia), it is easier to deal with a whole batch. Squash the berries so that the skin is thoroughly broken but the seeds are undamaged.*

2 *Berries vary in their softness, so make sure that the skins have been properly broken. As a rule, the riper the berries, the easier they are to squash. When sufficiently squashed, add sand to the berries.*

3 *Mix the sand and squashed berries well. The sand holds moisture and keeps the berries damp, thus speeding up the decomposition of the flesh. It also simulates the natural processes.*

4 *Choose an appropriately-sized pot and roughly fill it with the seed/sand mixture. Label it with the contents and the date they were put in. This will be useful if you have several pots. Firm down the mixture in the pots.*

5 *Place the pot or pots in a cold frame, or other convenient place, for the winter. Do not cover them. If mice could be a problem, fit fine mesh wire netting over the pots for protection.*

Collecting seeds

For the most part, saving seeds is fine, but not all seeds are worth saving; indeed, some are a waste of time. This applies principally to modern hybrid varieties, especially the F1 hybrids, which never come true from saved seed because they are the first generation of a cross between two distinct and selected parents. When saving seed, choose individual plants that are perhaps better than their neighbors or have characteristics that you like. Allow the seedheads to start drying out naturally. Collect them in a paper bag and hang this up to dry in a warm room or the greenhouse to ripen quickly. Once ready, shake the bag to release the seeds from their pods and keep them until the spring. Stored dry and cold, the seed will stay viable for some years. Of course, there are exceptions. Seeds from umbelliferous plants (carrots, parsnips, etc.) only stay viable for about a year. Saving flower seeds is great fun and tends to have more potential than saving vegetable seeds. In time, you could end up with your own strain of a particular variety of flower. Vegetables are hardly worth the trouble. The vast majority are hybrids and the progeny is usually inferior to the parent. However, beans and peas are usually worthwhile because you can save seed from the best plant(s) in a batch over the years and develop the strain until it could be better than the original – at least, under your conditions.

Poppies

Below: Put the capsules in a paper bag and hang in a warm room to ripen. Shake the seeds onto paper before storing in a small bottle or tub until spring.

Gather the capsules when the first few holes are open. The seeds tip out when you upend the ripe capsules.

Right: The poppy is one of the easiest flowers from which to save seed. All kinds develop a large seedhead that distributes seeds like a pepper pot.

Aquilegia

Below: Cut off the seedheads as they start to split. Place in bags in a warm, dry place to ripen. Store dry and cold until sowing in the spring.

Keep the seedheads in a bag and shake it so that the seeds collect in the bottom when they fall out of the capsule. Knock the seeds out gently.

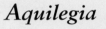

Above: Aquilegia seeds, other than those of long-spurred hybrids, are well worth saving. There is a wide variety of colors and flower sizes.

Stocks

Left: *Only plants with single flowers form seeds; fully double flowers are sterile. However, seeds will produce both single- and double-flowered plants. As the long seedpods do not open readily, even when the seed is ripe, you can safely hang the plants upside down to dry.*

Above: *To collect the seeds when the capsules are dry, twist the seedpod and it will split. It consists of two halves with a dividing membrane, so collect the seed from both halves.*

Delphiniums

Along with lupins, the delphinium is one of the most rewarding flowers from which to save seeds. Although the biggest and best are all named varieties and are hybrids, the seedlings that arise from their seeds come in so many shapes, sizes and colors that few need be wasted.

Left: *The elegant flower heads of delphiniums provide long-lasting displays during the summer. Saving and sowing the seeds can yield an attractive range of color variations.*

Below: *Cut an almost-ripe seedhead from a stem that is still green. It is important to leave the living stem on the plant, because the leaves will continue to feed the plant and build up its strength for the following year.*

Lavatera

Below: *The seed of annual lavatera is easy to save. The perennial lavatera, including the shrubby 'Barnsley' and other hybrids, is far less suitable; plants from the saved seed are poorer than the original.*

This is annual Lavatera trimestris 'Silver Cup'.

Above: *The seed capsules and seeds are reasonably large. Snip off the ripe, sandy-colored capsules and rub them between your hands. Store the seed that falls out for spring sowing.*

Dry the seedheads in a paper bag as described before.

Sowing very small seeds

1 When sowing half-hardy plant seeds, gently flatten (but do not firm) the surface of the seed or general-purpose mix with a presser.

2 Before sowing tiny seeds that will remain uncovered, sprinkle horticultural vermiculite or fine grade perlite on the surface of the mixture.

Horticultural vermiculite and perlite are extremely light materials that remain damp for some time.

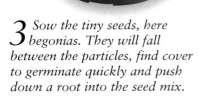

3 Sow the tiny seeds, here begonias. They will fall between the particles, find cover to germinate quickly and push down a root into the seed mix.

4 Water the seed by standing the pot in water until the surface is damp. Any other method is too drastic for the dustlike begonia seeds.

Sowing seeds

There are various methods of sowing seeds, depending on the kind of flower or vegetable, how it is being grown and when the seeds are being sown. If that sounds rather complicated, do not worry; it is really very simple and, in any case, instructions on sowing are given on nearly all seed packets. Hardy annuals are usually sown where they are to flower (*in situ*). You can also sow half-hardy annuals *in situ*, but because the seedlings would be killed by frost, either delay sowing them until the risk of frost is over or sow them in pots or trays in heat (greenhouse, windowsill, propagator or heated frame). Sow hardy biennials, such as wallflowers, and hardy perennials, such as delphiniums, in nursery rows in spring. Transplant the resulting seedlings into new nursery rows and, in the fall, transplant them again to where they will flower. Vegetables are treated in largely the same way except that some hardy ones, such as brassicas, are sown in nursery rows and then transplanted, whereas others, such as root vegetables are sown *in situ* and thinned out as seedlings. This is because the roots will not form properly if the seedlings are transplanted.

Above: *Some seeds, such as those of salvias and impatiens (shown here), require a relatively high temperature to germinate. This is where a heated propagator really comes into it own.*

Sowing medium-sized seeds

1 Sow larger seeds, such as these grasses, directly onto the surface of the flattened mix. Sprinkle them from a reasonable height for an even spread.

Sowing seeds into the ground

The simplest, and by far the most common method of sowing seeds, is to sow them directly into the ground. Break down the soil into a fine tilth. Run a taut garden line along the row where the seed is to be sown. With a draw hoe or stick, make a drill (a groove in the ground) to the recommended depth. Mark the drill with a stick at each end. Sprinkle the seeds evenly and thinly along the drill. Rake back the fine soil over the seeds so that they are covered to the recommended depth. If the soil is dry, water the drill gently but thoroughly. Finally, put in a plant label at one end of the drill.

Above: Sow hardy annual, biennial and perennial flower seeds, as well as hardy vegetable seeds, either where they are to mature in the garden or in nursery rows, as here.

2 Cover the seeds, gently releasing seed mix from your hand through a sieve. This distributes the mixture evenly, ensuring uniform germination.

3 Firm the mix gently to ensure that the seeds and mix are in close contact and the mix does not dry out too fast. This aids even germination.

4 After sowing, place the pot or seed tray carefully into a container of water and remove it when the surface darkens, showing it is damp.

5 Do not prick out grass seedlings singly; "patch" them out in groups. Ornamental grasses make a better show when planted out in clumps.

Sowing large seeds

1 Large seeds need much more room, both for their roots and top growth, so it is best to sow them individually, about 1in deep, in pots of seed or general potting mix. These are sunflower seeds.

2 Fill the planting hole by pushing the sides in with your fingers. Water large seeds from above with a fine-rosed watering can. Encourage children to start gardening with seeds like this.

Encouraging successful germination

Some seeds have special needs, either before or after sowing if they are to germinate successfully.

Seeds that need light to germinate include celery, lettuce, begonia, most grasses and many conifers. Seeds that need dark to germinate include angelica, rosemary, cyclamen, pansy and phacelia.

Begonia: Sow on the surface and keep at 70°F for 3-4 weeks.
Impatiens: Sow on the surface and ensure that the mix is uniformly moist but not wet. Keep sown seeds out of direct sunlight. Do not let the temperature drop below 70°F.
Pansy and violas: Sow seeds very shallowly 0.12in. Keep dark under aluminum foil or black plastic. Germinate the seeds at no less than 70°F.
Pelargoniums: For these seeds the optimum germination temperature

is 70-75°C. Keep the mixture uniformly moist.
Polyanthus: Do not allow the temperature to exceed 70°F. Surface sow and keep the mix moist to remove the growth inhibitor in the seed coat. Sprinkle a little mix on the surface once the seeds start to open.
Sweet peas: Apply a fungicidal seed dressing if possible and germinate at 50-68°F. Chip only the dark seeds, especially the blue-flowered varieties (see page 22).
Tomatoes: Sow 0.4in deep so that the seed coat remains underground, thus reducing the risk of seedling disease. The optimum germination temperature is 64-70°F.

Some seeds germinate at fairly high temperatures – often higher than might be expected, which is a good reason for using an electrically-heated propagator for these ones.

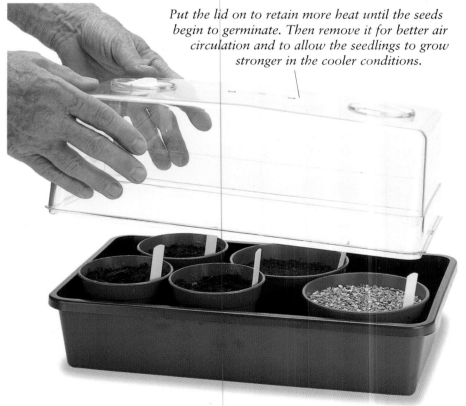

Put the lid on to retain more heat until the seeds begin to germinate. Then remove it for better air circulation and to allow the seedlings to grow stronger in the cooler conditions.

3 Put the pots into a propagator. This one, though unheated, will maintain a higher temperature than a room or greenhouse, so the seeds will germinate without the need for supplementary heat.

Nasturtiums in a tray

Nasturtiums also benefit from being sown in individual pots or, as here, a tray of pots. It avoids pricking out, as each seed is self-contained in its own pot. The only difference is that the pots are then placed in a seed tray for easier handling. Sow only one kind of plant in each tray, so that all the seeds appear more or less together.

1 Fill the tray with seed or general-purpose potting mixture. Place one seed into the middle of each small compartment.

Label the tray. You may recognise the seedlings as nasturtiums but you will not be able to tell colors apart.

2 When the seedlings reach this stage, stand the tray in the brightest position available. Even direct sunlight will not harm them, but remember to water them!

Below: These sunflowers have been sown early and raised under cover before planting out. This gives them a longer growing season and allows them to reach their full potential.

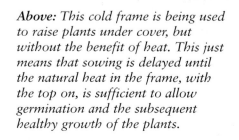

Above: This cold frame is being used to raise plants under cover, but without the benefit of heat. This just means that sowing is delayed until the natural heat in the frame, with the top on, is sufficient to allow germination and the subsequent healthy growth of the plants.

29

Pricking out petunias

1 *These petunia seedlings must be pricked out before the roots tangle together, making it difficult to tease them apart without breaking them.*

2 *Do not dig up seedlings from the pot; this will damage them. Invert the pot, give it a tap and the block of seedlings should drop into your hand.*

3 *Gently tease the soil block apart. Notice that the potting mix is thoroughly moist so that the plantlets are turgid and will send out new roots quickly once they are planted out.*

4 *Holding each seedling by a leaf, not the stalk, ease them out of the soil block one at a time. If a root is reluctant to come away, tease it out with a dibber.*

Pricking out and thinning seedlings

As soon as the two seed leaves have expanded, seedlings are judged large enough to handle and should be pricked out. This involves carefully easing them out of the seed mix with a small stick and replanting them into individual pots or in rows in a seed tray. There are two good reasons for doing this; first, the seedlings will be able to develop more strongly without the competition imposed by neighbors. Second, the seedlings are at far greater risk of succumbing to damping off fungus disease if they are left for too long in the pot where they were sown.

The container you use depends on the size of the seedlings. If they are small, space them evenly in a try or plant them individually in small pots. These containers can be clay or plastic or one of the degradable materials that can be left in place when the seedling are planted out later on. Larger seedlings, either through age or kind, should go straight into small pots. Once the seedlings have been pricked out, potted and watered in, stand the containers in a bright place where the seedlings will be able to grow strong and straight.

5 *Although commercial nurseries replant their seedlings at a close spacing, 2in is close enough and allows room for seedlings to develop.*

Pricking out tomato seedlings

Right: *When pricking out half-hardy vegetables, such as the tomato seedlings shown here, it is best to put them straight into 3in pots.*

Prick out tomatoes deeper than other seedlings, with the seed leaves just clear of the surface. The stem will readily put out roots, thus making a stronger plant.

Use a fine rose to avoid damaging the tiny plants.

6 *Give all the seedlings a good watering straight after pricking out. This will prevent them from wilting and also stimulates them to become established and grow quickly.*

Right: *Seeds of petunia F1 'Prism Sunshine' and many other F1 hybrids are expensive to buy. To prevent failures, provide the best possible conditions for propagation.*

Patching out lobelias

Right: *Instead of pricking them out singly, patch out lobelias in groups of three or four seedlings. This makes the plants more substantial.*

Left: *More than most other bedding plants, lobelias have stood the test of time. Today, there are more varieties with more colors and growth habits than ever. Even with their tiny seeds, they are easy to grow.*

Growing mixtures

Choosing the right growing mixture is important. If the seeds were sown in general-purpose mix, the seedlings can go into this as well. If the seeds were sown into seed or cuttings mixture, then ideally prick out the seedlings into potting mix. If you have no potting mixture, use general-purpose mix instead. As a rule, peat or peat-substitute mixes are best, but soil-based potting mixture is fine, so long as you buy it from a reliable source; there are a lot of sub-standard products on the market.

Using plug plants

Plug plants (usually ornamentals but also suitable vegetables) vary in age from a few days to many weeks, and are sold growing singly in appropriately-sized pots. The whole point of these seedlings and young plants is that gardeners can choose the exact number of plants they want, at just the right size and age, when they want them and without the trouble and expense of sowing and raising them. They obviously cost more than seeds but, when you consider the cost of a propagator, the electricity to run it, and the fact that you may have complete germination failures, the extra expense is minimal.

The most important thing to remember is that the smallest sizes will need pricking out or potting up within a few days of you getting them home. The little plants will probably have been grown at a higher temperature than you would normally use. This means that, to be on the safe side, you will need to cosset them for the first day or so and then gradually harden them off until they are used to your window or greenhouse conditions.

Fuchsia cuttings

Another excellent way of raising young plants is to insert cuttings straight into mix in small mesh pots. The roots grow through the holes so they can be potted up without removing the mesh pots. This lack of disturbance to the root system greatly reduces the chance of a check to their growth when they are potted on.

Below: Take fuchsia cuttings early in the growing season before the bush starts to flower. Remove flower buds from cuttings taken later on.

Left: Propagate named varieties of fuchsia, such as this 'Lye's Unique', by cuttings. Named varieties are tougher than they seem; many are hardy enough to live outdoors in temperate areas.

Lobelia plug plants

1 Because of the smallness of the seeds and seedlings, lobelia plug plants are sold in clumps, rather than as single plantlets.

2 These tiny plants will outgrow their plugs very quickly. After watering well, push them out with a dibber through the hole in the base.

3 Fill up 3in plastic pots with potting mixture and make a hole about the same size as the plugs. Plant one cluster in the centre of each pot.

4 Place the plug in the bottom of the hole and firm it gently into place. Give it a good watering before standing the pot in a bright position.

Geranium plug plants

1 Buying them as plug plants is a splendid way of giving you the sensation of growing your own plants from seeds or cuttings. These are sold in a little propagator, with pink water-retaining gel that keeps the seedlings moist.

2 These plantlets are at the right stage to pot up. Push out the individual seedlings from below with a dibber. If they have been kept well watered, the rootballs will come out easily and not fall apart when you handle them.

3 Using the same method as for lobelias, make a hole in the potting mix in each 3in plastic pot and drop a plug into it. Firm it very gently with your fingertips.

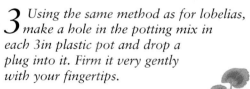

Above: *Geraniums make a superb greenhouse display. The majority are grown from late summer cuttings, but an increasing number of bedding varieties can be grown from seed. Many of these are sold as plug plants.*

Never firm the mix too hard or it may become waterlogged and the plants will collapse.

Suitable plants

Plug plants are an uneconomical way of acquiring small plants in very large quantities, but they are a boon to gardeners with an average-sized plot. The range of available plants is vast – from ageratum, aster and begonia to rudbeckia, salvia and verbena.

Dividing plants

One of the easiest ways of increasing the number of certain kinds of plants is by division. This is particularly appropriate for herbaceous plants because many, such as herbaceous phlox and Michaelmas daisies, form clumps over the years. These usually spread outwards by means of underground stems (rhizomes). Division involves splitting a clump into several smaller pieces and replanting them. The only proviso is that the plant must be one that spreads by means of rhizomes; lupins and dahlias, for example, are not good subjects for division. They send out new shoots in the spring from the base of those that grew the previous year. With these plants, the best method is to split the stem downwards and pull apart the tubers, leaving a short length of stem attached. It is buds at the base of the stem that give rise to new shoots; they do not come directly from the tubers.

To propagate a clump-forming plant, such as Michaelmas daisy (asters), you normally dig up the whole thing, pull it apart, retaining the younger portions on the outside, and throw away the older part in the middle. If you replant the pieces you keep, they will form several much smaller clumps in time. You can also do this with pot-grown plants just bought from a garden center. To divide one of these to make more than one plant out of it, knock it out of the pot and tease it apart into as many pieces as you can, remembering that to be viable, each new portion must have at least one growing shoot. Spring and fall are the best times of year for carrying out division. Mid- to late fall is marginally better because the recently divided sections will be well established by the time new growth starts in spring. However, spring planting is fine as long as you water the new plants as needed in the summer.

About: With their vibrant colors, crocosmia and its modern cultivars have improved dramatically in recent years. Divide overcrowded plants during the spring.

Herbaceous plants that can be divided

Acanthus, Achillea, Adiantum, Agapanthus, Ajuga, Anemone, Arabis, Armeria, Aruncus, Arundinaria, Aster, Bellis, Bergenia, Caltha, Carex, Centaurea, Chrysanthemum, Convallaria, Coreopsis, Cortaderia, Crocosmia, Delphinium, Dicentra, Doronicum, Epimedium, Eranthis, Erigeron, Euphorbia, Gaillardia, Gentiana, Geranium, Geum, Grasses and related plants, Helenium, Helianthus, Hemerocallis, Hosta, Iris (rhizomatous), Kerria, Kniphofia, Lamium, Liatris, Linaria, Liriope, Lychnis, Mentha, Monarda, Nepeta, Nymphaea, Ophiopogon, Osmunda, Oxalis, Penstemon, Phlox, Phormium, Phygelius, Physalis, Physostegia, Polemonium, Polyanthus, Potentilla (herbaceous), Pulmonaria, Pyrethrum, Ranunculus, Rheum, Rudbeckia, Salvia (herbaceous), Scabiosa, Sedum, Solidago, Stachys, Teucrium, Tradescantia, Trillium, Trollius, Verbascum, Verbena (herbaceous).

Dividing ophiopogon

1 This clump-forming plant is ideal for propagation by division. A potted plant from a garden center can often be divided straight away.

Dividing kniphofia

1 Dig a fork in close to the base of the plant to lever the clump out of the ground. Dig deeply to get as much of the root out as possible, and take care not to damage the stems.

2 As the clump emerges, you can see that it is made up of many smaller crowns pressed close together. When separated and given more space, they make good new plants.

3 Choose the best piece from the original clump to replant; ideally, this should have four or five good strong shoots, as here. Peel away any dead or broken leaves from the base.

Above: A superb display of red hot pokers (kniphofia) is only attainable if it is well cared for. Split up clumps every four to five years to maintain youth, vigor and plenty of flowers.

2 Push back the leaves and you can see the individual tufts of the plant. These probably grew from a single tuft that developed from basal buds.

3 Remove the plant and divide it into tufts of leaves, each with their own root system. Pot these up singly or plant them in their final position.

Dividing hostas

Existing hostas are probably best left undisturbed until they need dividing, as plants can be slow to re-establish. Leave those in the garden until the clump outgrows its space, the plants lack vigor, or the center of an old clump starts to die out. Lift and divide established hostas in early spring, ideally before the leaves start unfurling.

Dividing ornamental grasses

1 Clump-forming grasses, such as this elegant Stipa tenuissima, *divide easily. You can split up a new plant simply by removing it from its pot and dividing it into two roughly equal parts.*

2 *Pot up each section and leave it to establish a good root system and grow bigger. Use a soil-based potting mix at this stage, especially if the grass is to be planted outdoors.*

3 *Firm gently around the plant with your fingertips. Once the pot is reasonably full of roots, you can plant it outside in the border. This attractive grass likes a sunny spot.*

Above: *These well-established ornamental grasses began life as small sections from a large clump, divided in spring as growth was starting. The pale, silky flowerheads of the pampas grass,* Cortaderia selloana, *provide a backdrop to the reddish-brown spikes of the shorter* Miscanthus sinensis.

Dividing primroses

Many primroses, including primulas and polyanthus, are propagated by division. Wait until they finish flowering in the spring and then dig up the whole plant. You will see that it expands in a mainly upward direction, rather than outwards, by extending the stem that carries the flowers and leaves. This stem develops roots throughout its length. Snap off the rosette of leaves, together with about 1in of stem. Plant this to give you a new plant. A strong mother plant will yield up to six offspring.

Left: *The yellow* Primula veris *and orange* P. uralensis *create a colorful garden display. Division keeps them growing vigorously.*

Dividing a potted aster

1 *This aster is a new purchase from a garden center. An examination of the root system showed that it was large enough to be split into at least two clumps.*

2 *If the roots are sufficiently well developed, divide the original plant into two simply by carefully pulling it apart. You can then plant the pieces directly into the garden.*

Above: *Rejuvenate a clump of asters by dividing it into two or more sections. Use a spade or two garden forks back to back.*

Below: *One or two years after splitting up a clump, you can expect a stunning display. This is Aster novi-belgii 'Coombe Margaret'.*

Above: *Asters, here A. x frikartii 'Mönch', are typical of the clump-forming herbaceous plants that can be divided. As a rule, split up the clumps every four to five years. Judge this by the quality and quantity of flowers.*

Taking cuttings

If seeds are the most economical and the simplest way of propagating plants, cuttings must surely come second. However, there is a very important difference between seeds and cuttings. Seeds do not always produce plants that are identical to the parent; cuttings do. The reason is that seeds are the result of sexual reproduction between a male and a female, while cuttings are pieces of one plant, so the plants that grow from them are bound to be identical to that plant. The term "cuttings" covers an enormous range of materials, or parts, of the plant, but stem cuttings are the norm. As a rule, small tip cuttings of soft plant tissue root quicker than large cuttings of hard wood, which take the longest to root. On the following pages, we describe the methods of taking and rooting most common types of cuttings. These include soft, semi-ripe and hardwood stem cuttings, plus leaf and root cuttings.

Collecting the raw material

The most appropriate part of a plant to use as a cutting will vary with the plant. Stem cuttings are the most common, but several plants are propagated from root cuttings and some succulents from whole leaf cuttings.

Left: When taking cuttings, chose healthy material, with no sign of pests or diseases. As a rule, take cuttings from the outside of the plant, from the side facing the sun. These are stocky and sturdy and most likely to root quickly.

Preparing the cuttings

Attention to detail is important when taking cuttings. Having collected a suitable amount of raw material, select the best growths for making cuttings. Always use a sharp knife or blade. Leave as many leaves on the cutting as you can; they supply it with the carbohydrates that go to build the roots. Always make the bottom of the cutting immediately below a leaf joint and cut off the bottom leaf or pair of leaves. With small-leaved plants, you may need to remove more. The aim is to have 0.5-1in of bare stem at the base to place into the rooting mixture. Buried or half-buried leaves soon rot.

Below: To root ivy, take just one leaf and its accompanying axillary bud (the one at the base of the leaf stalk). Leave 1in of stem below the bud and push it into the rooting mixture.

Below: A typical stem cutting will be 2-3in long, depending on the vigor and leaf size of the plant. Remove the lower leaves, leaving just a few terminal ones to help build the new root system. Although leaves supply a cutting with carbohydrates, they also remove water from it. The aim is to strike a good balance.

Avoid any shoots with terminal flower buds.

Make a clean cut immediately below a leaf node.

Remove the bottom pair of leaves.

If these two leaves are large, remove them. If they are smaller, cut them in half.

Growing medium

When rooting cuttings in the garden, you may need to add sharp sand or grit to heavy clay soil to improve drainage. Sandy soil benefits from the addition of peat to help it retain moisture. In the greenhouse, use a proprietary cuttings mix or a 50/50 mix of moss peat and sharp sand.

Right: Hardwood cuttings taken in early winter are normally rooted in the ground. Correct signs of water-logging by adding grit and peat.

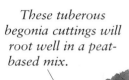

These tuberous begonia cuttings will root well in a peat-based mix.

Above: Although cuttings will not tolerate waterlogging, many are quite happy rooting in water. After potting up rooted cuttings, wean them gradually onto a potting mixture by starting off with a saturated mixture.

Soft basal cuttings of delphinium, lupin or tuberous begonia may be quite large and a useful trick is to half-fill the pot with mix so that the cuttings can lean against the side of the pot for support.

Above: Most soft and semi-ripe cuttings will root in a cuttings mixture. A 5in pot or half-pot is fine for about four or five cuttings.

Potting up

When the cuttings have rooted they need to go into pots of their own. The old rooting mixture will have insufficient nutrients in it to support the growing plants, and feeding them is not the solution because they have also run out of root room. The mix into which you root cuttings is largely a matter of personal preference, because the manufacturers have made it easy. In essence, use either a potting or a multipurpose mix. If you are potting up heathers, rhododendron or other acid-loving plants, use a mixture blended to meet their needs.

Above: Gently separate the rooted cuttings, damaging the root systems as little as possible. This is easy if the root systems are still small, but if you have left the job too long, it can be difficult. Put a little potting mixture in the bottom of the new pots. Place the rooted cutting on top and fill up the pot with more mix.

Never over-firm the mixture. This will force out the air and cause it to become waterlogged.

Right: Firm the cutting in gently with your fingers and water it well – until you see water coming out of the base of the pot.

Cuttings in water

One of the easiest ways of rooting many cuttings is in a jar of water. Unfortunately, not all subjects respond equally well to this method, but most soft-growing houseplants and many woody hardy plants are very successful. The best time to root cuttings in water is during the growing season, from mid-spring to early fall, when there is ample warmth and, more importantly, daylight. This also allows you time to pot them up, so that soil-adapted roots are formed before winter. Because roots form most readily from young tissue, take cuttings from the tip of the current year's new shoots. Make sure they come from growth that is healthy and stocky, not thin and straggly. Cut the base just below a leaf or pair of leaves. Remove the bottom leaf or leaves before placing the cutting in a jar of ordinary tapwater. Alternatively, take the cutting with a heel of older wood. The length of the cutting is largely immaterial, but bear in mind that the younger growth sends out roots most readily, so a large cutting is less suitable than one that is, say, 3-4in long.

1 Woody shrubs, such as this rosemary, root well in water. Take a heel cutting off an older shoot, tidy the base and remove the lower leaves.

2 Half-fill the jar with tapwater. There should be enough water in the jar to prevent the cuttings from wilting in the first few days.

3 After a few weeks there will be a healthy crop of roots and the shoot itself will have grown. Pot it up now; it will soon need nourishment.

4 These roots are not at all like the ones that form on a cutting rooted in potting mixture. They have formed in water and will need to adapt to growing in soil.

5 *Pot the cuttings into a peat-based or similar mix. This is the most suitable type because it holds a large amount of water and is very easy for the new roots to grow into.*

Suitable plants

A great many plants will form roots if they are stood in water, and really it is a question of trial and error. For the most part, it is softwood and herbaceous cuttings that succeed best. This is simply because their soft and tender shoots produce roots more quickly than woodier cuttings. However, it is true that cuttings of rosemary, lavender and many other woody plants will root very well in a glass jar at a sunny window, even though they take longer than softer ones. Remember that it is only the shoots that form roots and not the leaves of plants.

6 *Gently firm down the mix without damaging the roots. They will be quite brittle. A lightly firmed mix will contain abundant oxygen – vital for roots.*

Above: *Rosemary is a lovely small shrub in its own right, as well as a useful herb. It thrives in dry conditions and its many erect stems with grayish green leaves are a joy in winter. The pale blue flowers are especially useful to bees and other nectar-seeking insects. After 10-12 years, the plant becomes leggy and bare, but is very easy to propagate.*

Rooting cuttings

Stand the cuttings at a sunny window, where they will quickly root. This is important with all cuttings; the longer they remain without roots, the more likely they are to die. Cuttings that root quickly always thrive. If the water turns green and smelly, change it. The time taken for cuttings to root varies. A soft cutting, such as busy Lizzie, should start to root within a couple of weeks and will be ready for potting up a week or so later.

Carnation pipings

For reasons that are not clear, carnation cuttings are known as pipings. In this context, carnations includes all the perennial members of the *Dianthus* genus, such as border carnations (outdoors), perpetual flowering carnations (greenhouse) and all the different species and cultivars of hardy pinks. Many of the species do come true from seed, so this is the obvious way to propagate them. However, most others, including the named varieties of carnation and pink, need to be propagated vegetatively. This means taking the piping from a shoot with no flower bud at the top, so that the cutting can root without having to compete with the flower for sap. You may have to search hard to find a flowerless shoot because some varieties flower profusely and finding a "blind" shoot can be difficult. There is a slight distinction between normal cuttings and pipings. Cuttings are taken by *cutting* the top section of stem away and rooting it, whereas pipings are *pulled* from the end of a shoot so that a small section of stem is removed from inside the leaf joint. Both pipings and cuttings can be taken at any time during the summer. Pinks and carnations can also be propagated by layering. To do this, split the stem at the point that is to be buried. After pegging down and covering this section, roots will form at the wound and you can separate the layer from the parent a few weeks later when the roots have formed.

Right: Dianthus 'Pink Charm' is one of many pinks that bloom over a long period in summer and make splendid garden flowers. They are especially fond of a dry, sunny bank, where they can bask in the warmth.

1 You can tell that this pink needs replacing. There are few flowers and twisted, leafless and brown stems towards the base. The few remaining shoots will make good cuttings.

Pinks and carnations are shortlived plants; replace or take cuttings every three or four years.

2 Take the piping from an old section of plant. One good way is to pull it off and shorten it to a cutting if the break is in the wrong place.

3 Root the pipings in cells about 2in deep. Carnations and pinks root at about the same time. Being in cells they will separate easily.

Below: Perpetual carnations should succeed beyond the year of flowering, but need good care. Few are scented, but they still make good cut flowers.

The roots in this cell are well formed and have reached the sides. There is no hurry to pot up a young plant at this stage but do it within the next 10-14 days.

4 A few weeks later the cuttings are ready for potting up singly or planting out. Which you do depends on the season and whether the plants are hardy pinks, border carnations or perpetual carnations.

5 Pot the rooted cuttings into 3in pots, using a peat, or peat-substitute potting or multipurpose mix. Potting mix is best because it is made specifically for potting up.

Soft cuttings

Many plants propagated from soft cuttings are herbaceous in nature and are raised in this way using very young shoots in spring. A few, including pelargoniums, are also grown from soft cuttings but later in the growing season. Pelargoniums, commonly known as geraniums, are half-hardy plants that can be grown in pots or as bedding. Zonals have furry, sometimes banded (zoned) leaves, whereas regals are completely green with less hairy leaves and showier flowers. In recent years it has become possible to raise zonals from seed, but cuttings are still the only reliable way of propagating named varieties of zonals and regals. Neither can be grown from seed with any chance of coming true to the parent. (This also applies to scented-leaved species and hybrids.) Take cuttings in late summer, when the shoots are still soft but beginning to ripen from the base. The cuttings root in a month or so, grow on steadily and are ready for planting outside the following spring, in flower, when the risk of frost is over. You can take cuttings in spring, but zonals will take many more weeks to attain flowering size.

Irishman's cuttings

Always be on the lookout for a shoot originating from the base of the plant. You may find that the underground part of the shoot has produced roots. Use it. It is called an Irishman's cutting. Pot it into a 3.5in pot of seed mixture, firm it in gently and water. Place the cutting in a propagator or plastic bag in a shady spot for four to six weeks.

1 This zonal pelargonium will provide several good cuttings. It is growing in a pot but could equally well be in a border outside. First you must decide which shoots will make the best cuttings.

2 Take a cutting 3-4in long from just below a leaf joint. Shorter cuttings root more quickly, but also die more quickly. Longer ones need more time to root.

Flowers will weaken the cutting if not removed.

3 Once you have removed a shoot, it is important to cut away certain parts to make it into a cutting, otherwise rooting will be delayed. In addition, some of the pieces may rot if allowed to remain.

Do not remove too many leaves; they "feed" the cutting.

Bracts occur at each leaf joint and may rot if left on.

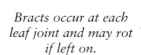

Cut off the lower leaves that would be buried.

4 Aim to put five or six cuttings into a 5in half-pot. If there is not enough room, they may be too large. If too much room, they could be too small. Put one in the center. Firm the cuttings in gently.

5 Water in the cuttings and keep them in a cool, shady place. They may not need any more water; pelargoniums are fleshy plants and water is stored in the stem and leaves.

6 The lower level of staging in a greenhouse is an ideal place to put the cuttings. If you put them on top, cover them with a single thickness of newspaper for shade until they root.

Suitable plants

Achillea, Aubretia, Ballota, Buddleia, Caryopteris, Centranthus, Cerastium, Chamaemelum, Cheiranthus, Chrysanthemum, Codonopsis, Corylopsis, Delphinium, Euphorbia, Exochorda, Fremontodendron, Fuchsia, Gypsophila, Halesia, Hebe, Iberis, Linaria, Linum, Lippia, Lupin, Lysimachia, Mentha, Mimulus, Nepeta, Oenothera, Origanum, Penstemon, Pyrethrum, Saponaria, Sedum, Silene, Spiraea, Thalictrum, Thymus, Tropaeolum, Veronica.

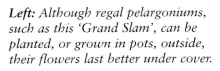

Left: *Although regal pelargoniums, such as this 'Grand Slam', can be planted, or grown in pots, outside, their flowers last better under cover.*

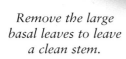

Semi-ripe cuttings

The term "semi-ripe" refers to a tree or shrub cutting that is taken in mid- and late summer. The shoot might still be growing, or it could have stopped for that season. In either case, the tip should still be relatively soft, although the base will be hardening. Depending on the plant species, the non-flowering cutting should be 2-4in long, excluding the leaves. It can be a tip cutting taken from the end of a shoot of the current season's growth or, more usually, it is a heel cutting; a short and complete shoot of the current season's growth pulled off an older shoot, with a fragment of the older shoot attached. This can look a bit like a foot, hence the term "heel cutting." As a rule, heel cuttings root quicker in mid- and late summer than tip cuttings, so bear this in mind when collecting cuttings material. Collect material from the sunny or brightest side of the tree or shrub, where the shoots are shorter and stockier, and make sure they are pest- and disease-free. As you collect the cuttings, place them in a plastic bag to prevent them wilting as far as possible. One big advantage of propagating from semi-ripe cuttings is that you do not need a greenhouse or even a sunny window. They will root in the ground or in pots or trays of suitable mixture. However, they must be enclosed to prevent wilting. On a small scale, a plastic bag over the pot is sufficient, but if you plan to insert a number of cuttings in the ground, make sure that you will be able to cover them all with cloches or a cold frame. Semi-ripe cuttings are the easiest way of propagating many popular trees and shrubs.

1 *In the case of hydrangeas, take tip cuttings, rather than heel cuttings. Because of the plant's large leaves and long shoots, tip cuttings are more convenient and root better.*

Remove the large basal leaves to leave a clean stem.

Discard this piece of stem so that the base of the cutting is at a leaf joint.

2 *Trim the base of the cutting immediately below a pair of leaves. Cut off the leaves as cleanly and as close to the stem as possible.*

3 *Because they are so large, cut the biggest leaves in half. This reduces transpiration and makes it easier to accommodate the cuttings. It does not delay rooting at all, as there is still ample leaf area to "feed" the cutting while it is rooting.*

4 *Dip the base of the cutting in hormone rooting powder. This encourages the formation of a callus from which new roots will grow.*

5 Place a couple of cuttings in a pot of sowing or cuttings mixture. Hydrangea roots easily; you do not need many to get one or two plants.

6 Water the cuttings until you see the water seeping out around the base of the pot. One good watering will usually last until the cuttings root.

7 To keep the cuttings damp, place the pot in a plastic bag, push in a drinking straw, twist the neck of the bag and blow into it. Put a wire twist around the neck.

Above: *Hydrangeas are among the more flamboyant flowering shrubs. This is* Hydrangea macrophylla, *the mophead or hortensia type.*

Above: *Hydrangea paniculata is one of the more decorative and unusual hydrangeas. This is 'Tardiva'; its numerous ray florets make it a show-stopper in any garden in the fall.*

8 Two split canes pushed into the mix also help to stop the bag collapsing onto the cuttings. Condensation shows that there is plenty of moisture for the cuttings.

Suitable plants

Abelia, Abutilon,
Anthemis, Arabis,
Armeria, Aucuba,
Berberis, Buxus,
Calluna, Camellia,
Caryopteris, Ceanothus,
Ceratostigma, Choisya,
Cistus, Coronilla,
Cotinus, Cotoneaster,
Cytisus, Daphne,
Dianthus, Diervilla,
Dipelta, Drimys,
Elaeagnus, Erica,
Erodium, Escallonia,
Eucryphia, Euonymus,
Fatshedera, Fatsia,
Forsythia, Fothergilla,
Fuchsia, Garrya,
Gaultheria, Genista,
Hebe, Helianthemum,
Helichrysum, Hibiscus,
Hydrangea, Hypericum,
Iberis, Ilex, Jasminum,
Juniperus, Kalmia,
Kerria, Lavandula,
Lavatera, Ligustrum,
Lonicera, Myrtus,
Nandina, Olearia,
Osmanthus, Pachysandra,
Philadelphus, Phlomis,
Photinia, Pieris,
Pittosporum, Polygonum,
Potentilla, Prunus
laurocerasus, Pyracantha,
Rosemary, Salvia,
Sambucus, Santolina,
Senecio, Skimmia,
Solanum, Syringa,
Taxus, Ulex, Viburnum,
Vinca, Weigela.

Below: To keep honeysuckle shrubs in good shape, clip the young plants regularly from their first full growing season. Left to their own devices, they soon put on lax, top-heavy growth. This is Lonicera nitida 'Bagessen's Gold'.

Below: Philadelphus 'Belle Etoile' is a compact cultivar that grows up to 6ft high. The single, highly scented flowers appear in early summer. Take semi-ripe cuttings after flowering.

Propagating lonicera

1 Lonicera nitida *is easily propagated at home. Take short pieces from the strong shoots on the current year's growth that have been left unclipped.*

These side shoots are ideal for cuttings.

Propagating philadelphus

1 *This philadelphus (mock orange) has plenty of appropriately-sized shoots for propagating on the more twiggy sections of growth. Avoid strong new shoots.*

2 *Cut off the strip of bark that came away from the parent shoot. It will play no part in the rooting process and may well rot if left on.*

2 In a sheltered spot in the garden, make a hole in the prepared ground with a dibber. Dip the base of the cutting in hormone rooting powder and put it into the hole.

3 Firm the cutting in gently so that it is held in place, with all parts of the buried stem in contact with the soil. Repeat the process with more cuttings as needed.

4 With a few cuttings in place, give them a good watering. You should not need to water them again. Do not delay watering until all the cuttings are in; the early ones might wilt before you have finished.

5 Cover the cuttings. A double-walled plastic tent is a good insulator. Inside the tent the cuttings will be warmer than outside and the tent will prevent excessive water loss.

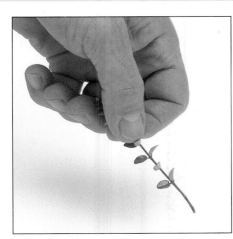

5 Label and date the cuttings, put the pot in a plastic bag and tie up the top. Choose a bag that is both tall and wide enough to surround the pot without touching or disturbing the cuttings inside.

3 Remove two or three pairs of leaves from the base, leaving a clean stem 1in long. Leaves are also a potential source of disease.

4 Pack small cuttings closely in a suitably sized pot filled with a 50/50 mix of peat and sand or a proprietary seed and cutting mix. Firm in lightly.

Hardwood cuttings

Taking a hardwood cutting simply involves pushing a shoot taken from a shrub into the ground and waiting for it to sprout leaves. It is a cheap and easy way to propagate and can be done outdoors without any form of protection for the cuttings. However, by no means everything will succeed and it is a slow method, and the longer a cutting takes to root, the greater the chances of it dying. On the other hand, the woodier a cutting is, the longer it will survive without roots.

Late fall and early winter are the best times to take the cuttings, but not too soon after leaf-fall. Take the cutting from the current season's growth. There is very little advantage in using hormone rooting powder or liquid, nor is it necessary to take cuttings with a heel. Once planted, the bottom end of the cutting will form a callus on the wound during the winter, and it is from this tissue that roots will be put out during the following spring and summer. Normally, cuttings will have formed enough roots to be safely moved one year later. Certain species, such as willows, will root much quicker than others and can be moved sooner. However, it is seldom worth it and it is best to postpone lifting hardwood cuttings until the fall or winter after they were taken.

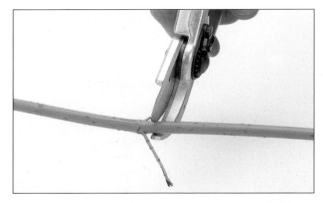

1 You can take material for cuttings from any part of a tree or shrub, but choose suitably thick, ripe wood, completely free of pests and diseases. This will normally be on the outside of a plant and on the sunny side.

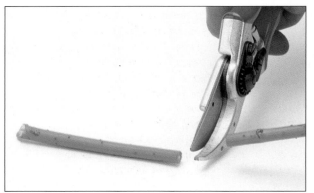

2 Make a cut just above a pair of buds. If you leave more than 0.5in of shoot above the top bud, there is a risk that it will become infected and the cutting may die.

This is the best material for cuttings: a single, stout piece.

3 Allowing 6in for the cutting, trim the base below a pair of buds. Trees and shrubs vary in their need for the bottom of a cutting to be below a bud, so treat them all the same.

4 All these shoot sections would make suitable cuttings. The one on the right is the least appropriate. It is too thin and the many side shoots could easily die during the winter.

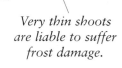

Very thin shoots are liable to suffer frost damage.

This is the least suitable piece, but should still form roots.

Left: Propagate blackcurrant bushes by hardwood cuttings taken as soon as the leaves have dropped in the fall. Make the cuttings 12in long and insert them so that only the top two or three buds are showing above the ground.

Left: Gooseberries are always grown on a "leg" (a short trunk), so only bury them for about half their length. However, the hardwood cuttings should still be 12in long.

Above: These vivid winter stems of Cornus stolonifera 'Flaviramea' – a major feature of the plant's garden display – can be used to provide plenty of hardwood cuttings.

5 To prepare a planting area for the cuttings, loosen the soil, then push in a spade vertically and lever it back to open a V-shaped slit. A vertically planted cutting has the best chance of developing into a well-shaped plant.

6 Push the cuttings into the V slit until only 1in is showing. This may seem deep, but in many species, the whole length of buried shoot produces roots, ensuring that a large root system develops quickly.

7 Firm down the soil with your heel or, as here, a closed fist. It ensures that there are no air spaces in the soil, where roots will not form, that the soil is in contact with the cutting and that it does not dry out too quickly.

Suitable plants

Plants that can be propagated from hardwood cuttings include: Ampelopsis, Buddleia, Celastrus, Cornus, Deutzia, Diervilla, Fallopia baldschuanica, Ficus, Forsythia, Jasminum, Kerria, Laburnum, Leycesteria, Ligustrum, Metasequoia, Morus, Parthenocissus, Perovskia, Philadelphus, Populus (poplar), Ribes (ornamental and fruiting currants, and gooseberries), Rosa, Salix, Sambucus, Santolina, Spiraea, Symphoricarpos, Tamarix, Viburnum, Weigela, Wisteria.

Leaf cuttings

1 *Snap off fully mature but still completely green, healthy leaves as cuttings.*

The important thing about leaf cuttings is that they are not the same thing as leaf *bud* cuttings. The latter are specialised stem cuttings in which one leaf and its accompanying bud are used as cuttings and the new plant develops from the bud. With leaf cuttings, you remove the whole leaf from the stem without any bud and push the cut base either into a seed and cuttings mixture or an equal mix of peat and coarse sand. The base of the leaf heals over under the mixture and then produces roots. However, that is only half the story, because a leaf with roots is not much use. After a few more weeks, a small plant, or cluster of plants, develops amongst the roots and it is from these that the new plant develops. No rooting hormone powder is needed.

While this is quite a common way of propagating several houseplants, such as African violets, *Begonia rex* and streptocarpus, very few hardy plants are suitable subjects. The catch is that, like all cuttings, the leaves must stay alive long enough for roots to form on the cut base. This means that the method is only appropriate for plants with thick, fleshy leaves. Here, we are using *Sedum spectabile*, but it works equally successfully with most other sedums. In fact, it is the ability of this plant's leaves to root and form new plants that makes it so invasive. An apparently similar situation occurs with the piggyback plant, *Tolmiea menziesii*. However, the important difference there is that it develops and carries actual plantlets on the upper surface of its leaves.

2 *Retain as many leaves as you will need. Remove the base cleanly with a sharp knife. This is not vital, but removes any torn and dead tissue that might otherwise develop a fungus infection.*

3 Push each leaf about 1in into the mixture, so that the base stays dark and moist and the leaf remains upright. Firm the mix down gently with your fingers. It should remain open in texture.

Use good-quality leaves; avoid damaged or diseased ones.

4 With all the leaves in the mix, water the tray well with a fine-rosed watering can. Stand it in a sunny spot to encourage quick rooting. Make sure that the potting mixture does not dry out at any time.

5 Stand the tray in a greenhouse or at a sunny window. There is no reason why you should not place it in a cold frame outdoors. The only proviso is that you must take the leaf cuttings earlier to allow more time for them to root.

Below: Sedum 'Brilliant' is a good cultivar of S. spectabile, *but there are many others. The flowers appear at a time when the borders need cheering up in late summer and early fall.*

Root cuttings

Taking sections of root and using them to produce new plants seems an unlikely method of propagation, but you only have to think of weeds such as dandelions and docks to realise how natural it is. If these weeds are beheaded with a hoe, new shoots soon emerge to replace the original crown. What happens is that adventitious buds on the roots have grown into new shoots. Adventitious buds are growth buds hidden in the creases of thick, fleshy roots for just this purpose. Many of the thicker-rooted plants can be increased in this way, as can many creeping plants (think of bindweed and ground elder). Take root cuttings in early winter. It is better for the plant whose roots are providing the cuttings; radical damage like this would seriously affect a growing plant. Stand the pots or trays in cold frames for the winter, and the cuttings will start sending up shoots in spring. The best way to take root cuttings from herbaceous plants is to dig down one side of a dormant clump and use the pieces of root that are severed. Once you have enough, replace the soil in the hole and tread it down. By the time growth starts again during the spring, the plant will have "forgotten" that anything has happened to it and recover its original vigor.

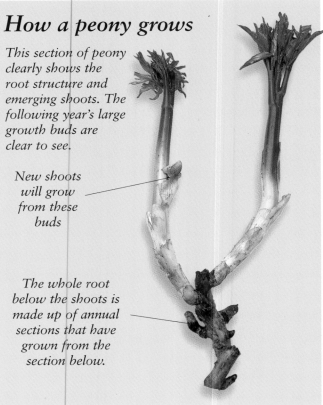

How a peony grows

This section of peony clearly shows the root structure and emerging shoots. The following year's large growth buds are clear to see.

New shoots will grow from these buds

The whole root below the shoots is made up of annual sections that have grown from the section below.

Above: *This piece of peony root is ideal propagation material. You can even see the "eyes" that will develop into shoots and roots. This young root in active growth will soon "strike" (root).*

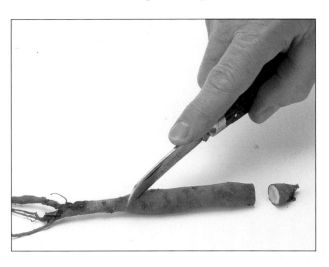

1 *Cut the top end straight and the bottom end slanting, so that you know which end should be uppermost when you insert the cuttings.*

2 *Place the cuttings into a 3in pot of cuttings mixture or a 50/50 peat/sand mixture, with the slanting cut edge downwards.*

3 *Push the cutting straight down so that the top is about 0.5in below the surface of the mixture. Put two cuttings into each pot.*

Phlox

Herbaceous phlox is a very common host of stem eelworm. However, this damaging pest is never found in the roots, so by taking root cuttings you can be sure that the disease will not be carried over to the cuttings.

1 Start by removing the plant from its pot and teasing off as much potting mix as possible so that you can clearly see the roots. The best ones for propagating are white and healthy and about as thick as a piece of string.

2 Bundle the cuttings together and cut them all into 3in lengths. Although they are root cuttings, there is no need to cut the ends straight and slanting as for peony cuttings; they will not be planted in a pot.

3 Lay the cuttings out flat in a tray, about 1in apart. This gives them plenty of room to develop but is not wasteful of space. These are lying in a cuttings mixture, but it could just as well be a mix of 50/50 peat and grit.

4 Once the tray is full of cuttings, cover the root sections evenly with about 0.5in of the same cuttings mixture. Firm the mixture gently into place and water the tray well before putting it in a warm place.

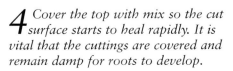

4 Cover the top with mix so the cut surface starts to heal rapidly. It is vital that the cuttings are covered and remain damp for roots to develop.

Above: Phlox paniculata 'Red Indian'. Phlox can be propagated by root cuttings or, if free of eelworm, by soft cuttings in spring or division in winter.

Left: Root cuttings are the best way to produce several plants of herbaceous peonies, here P. 'Nancy Lindsay'. For one or two plants, division works well.

Poppy root cuttings

1 The root of the brightly colored Oriental poppy looks more like an exotic root vegetable. It is easily propagated from sections of its thick, fleshy roots.

Below: These Oriental poppies put on a vivid display in the garden. Use root cuttings to propagate named varieties, or sow some of the copiously produced seed for new plants if you are not worried about keeping to the same variety.

2 Dig up the whole plant or just an outside clump if it is a large one. Tease the roots and stems apart. Do not worry if breakages should occur; the roots will be chopped up anyway.

3 Not every root is as straight as a carrot, but all carry adventitious buds that will grow out into shoots. New roots will grow from the sides of the cutting. Cut the root into pieces 3-4in long.

Use a clean sharp knife to make smooth, not jagged, cuts.

4 Make a straight cut at the top and a slanted one at the base so that you know which end to plant uppermost. If you get it wrong, a plant will still develop but it takes longer.

A slanted cut tells you that this is the bottom end of the root.

A straight cut reminds you that this is the top.

Simple root cuttings

If you want only one or two new plants, you can usually produce them more easily by using just the top 2-3in of each root, according to the type of plant.

1 Buds are clearly visible on the top section. In fall, when the root is becoming dormant, you can pull or cut off green growth.

2 The top of the cutting is at the righthand end of this length of root. Cut off the unwanted basal section with the usual slanting cut.

3 Space out the cuttings to give them plenty of room. They will grow into small plants before you move them the following fall.

4 Push the cuttings into the mix. As the buds are well developed, they will grow out easily and need not be buried. Label the container.

5 Fill a 3.5-5in pot with a cuttings mixture or a 50/50 mix of peat and grit. Push in a few root sections about 1.5in apart, with the flat end of the cutting at the top.

6 Push the cuttings in so that the tops are just buried. This ensures that all the buds stay damp and alive and will grow out into shoots or roots, according to their structure.

Suitable plants

Plants with fleshy roots that carry adventitious buds are suitable for propagation by root cuttings. These include: Ailanthus, Anchusa, Anemone x hybrida (japonica), Campsis, Catalpa, Catananche, Ceanothus, Clerodendron, Convolvulus, Crambe, Dicentra, Echinops, Embothrium, Eryngium, Geranium, Humulus, Limonium, Papaver orientale, Paulownia, Phlox paniculata, Physalis, Primula denticulata, Pulsatilla, Rhus typhina, Robinia, Romneya, Rubus cockburnianus, Symphytum, Verbascum.

Propagating sempervivum

1 *Sempervivum produces plantlets on the end of short "umbilical" stems. As these are fairly stiff, separating a plantlet is more appropriate than leaving it attached to the parent. Roots are produced from the joining stem.*

Using runners and plantlets

In the world of plant propagation, increasing your stock by runners and plantlets is undeniably easy. What we are talking about is plants that produce "babies" on the end of long or short stalks and it is these, rather than seeds, that give rise to the next generation. All you normally need to do is provide conditions under which the rootless plantlet will form roots. There are two ways of doing this. Either remove the plantlet and root it in a propagator or under mist, or leave it attached to the parent and encourage it to root into potting mix or into the ground. Leaving the plantlet attached requires less skill and attention, but detaching it first and rooting it in a pot is often quicker, given the right conditions, and the result is a plant that can go wherever you want it. Using unrooted and small, almost unformed plantlets requires more skill, but gives you more new plants more quickly. Rooting runners and plantlets is best carried out as early in the growing season as possible. However, suitable material is seldom available before halfway through the season. In many ways, this form of propagation resembles layering. However, here the plantlets are already forming, whereas with layering all you have is a bud that is required to grow into the new plant.

2 *Fill a half-pot with a 50/50 mix of peat (or substitute) and grit for extra drainage. This is important, otherwise the succulent leaves can rot.*

3 *Push the plantlet into the mix until the bottom leaves rest on the surface. This allows you to bury a good length of stem to form roots.*

4 *A 3-4in half-pot will comfortably hold five sempervivum plantlets. They will result in a cluster or rooted plants that can be planted without disturbance, giving you a respectable group straightaway.*

Right: *This is Sempervivum 'Commander Hay'. It produces many satellite plants around the central one. If the joining stems are pegged down, it will quickly form new plants.*

Propagating strawberries

1 Leave the runners attached to the mother plant while rooting. Bury a 3in pot of potting or seed mixture near the parent and plantlet.

2 Bring the plantlet to the pot and push it into the mixture. Hold it down securely with a thin piece of wire 8in long and bent in half.

3 Thoroughly water the plantlet, now pegged in place and under no strain. Keep the potting mix moist during the rooting period but not wet.

4 After about a month, the plantlet will have formed a root system. Separate the new plant when roots appear through the bottom of the pot.

5 The new plant can either be kept in its pot or be planted at once in its new, permanent position. The latter course is preferable, because the plant will be able to establish itself before winter.

6 Make sure that the planting hole is deep enough to bury the whole rootball but not the crown of the plant. That must remain above the ground.

Suitable plants

Relatively few plants can be propagated using runners and plantlets. These include members of the agave family, frageria (strawberry), sempervivum and tolmiea.

Do not use strawberry seeds for propagation. The seedlings will not be identical to the parent.

Above: The following summer, less than a year after propagation, you can expect a crop of luscious fruit. If planting is delayed until after mid-autumn, the crop weight is reduced.

Bulbs, corms and tubers

The best way of increasing bulbs and corms is to lift them when they are dry and dormant and save the small bulbils or cormlets that you dig up with the recently flowered parent. Daffodil and other narcissus bulbs split after flowering and it is these new, smaller bulbs that you save. Plant them in rows in the following early fall and they will emerge in spring to grow into larger bulbs. It is this need to enlarge before they will flower that has led to the belief that second year narcissus bulbs are "blind." Nothing of the sort, they are merely too small to flower. Hyacinth bulbs produce a ring of baby bulbs around the basal plate. Gather these when the parent is dormant and treat them as you would narcissi. Gladiolus corms also produce cormlets. Gather them as before, but do not plant them until the following spring. Crocus corms produce one or two new corms on top of the old flowered one, which dries up. Propagating these plants is, therefore, more or less self-regulating; all you have to do is collect the result.

Dahlia tubers

Botanically and structurally, dahlia tubers are quite different from potato tubers. Their sole job is to supply the dormant buds at the base of the stem with food and nutrients to enable them to grow into new stems the following spring. Dahlias are not propagated by means of their tubers; any tubers that become parted from the main clump will not survive and produce a new plant unless they include a small section of stem that carries one or more buds. Propagate named varieties by means of the new shoots that grow from the base of the stem in the spring. Cut off the shoots when they are 2-3in tall and root them as cuttings in a 50/50 peat/sand mixture.

Above: Propagate named varieties of dahlia such as these from cuttings, or split the clumps of stored tubers in spring. Grow the smaller bedding dahlias from seed sown each spring.

Right: To increase their number and improve flowering, dig up clumps of bulbs every few years. Once replanted in late summer or early fall, they will have more room to grow and thrive.

Left: Split up clumps of daffodils and other narcissi every three to four years. Otherwise, the bulbs keep splitting to produce offspring that take many years to reach flowering size.

Left: In common with all other bulbs and corms, gladioli must be propagated vegetatively if you want the progeny to be an exact copy of the parent plant. Save the little cormlets from around the base of the corm and sow them in the spring.

Dividing tulip bulbs

1 After flowering, leave the tulip to grow until the foliage yellows. Dig it up, clean it and remove the old stem. The single bulb will have divided into several smaller ones.

2 Gently tease apart the bulbs. Most will have a protective brown skin; leave it intact. The bulbils should break away easily from the dried-up basal plate that carried the roots.

Discard the original skin and roots.

3 The bulbils will vary enormously in size; the largest may be big enough to flower the following spring. All are worth keeping and replanting; even the smallest will flower within about three years.

Small bulbs need to be grown on before they reach flowering size.

This main bulb will flower the following spring.

Collecting tiger lily bulbils

1 Tiger lilies develop small bulbils in the leaf axils. When ripe, these fall to the ground, root and grow much like seeds.

2 Collect the bulbils in late summer. When ripe, they part easily. Some will have roots. Store them in cool peat until spring.

3 Fill a pot with seed or general-purpose mixture and press in the bulbils 1in apart. They will not become overcrowded.

4 Water, label and stand the pot in a cold frame until fall. The following spring, plant the bulbs 2in deep in nursery rows.

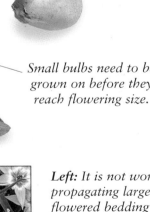

Left: It is not worth propagating large-flowered bedding tulips, as bought ones flower better and more reliably. The smaller and daintier specie tulips are easily increased from bulbils. This is *Tulipa aucheriana*.

Blackberry

Right: There are several variations on the theme of layering. The easiest way to produce just one or two new blackberry plants is by tip layering.

The shoot tip should be flexible enough to bend without too much stress.

Layering

Without doubt, layering is the easiest and most successful method of propagating a wide range of shrubs and climbers. It involves bending down a shoot or small branch of the plant you want to propagate and burying a short section of it so that roots form on the buried part. A growing season or so later, separate the layered portion with its roots from the parent plant, dig it up and plant it where it is to grow. The big virtue of propagating woody plants by layering is that it is nearly always successful and thus provides the propagating answer for plants that may be difficult to root in other ways. It is not difficult to see why this should be so; it is because the part of the layered shoot that will form the new plant remains attached to the parent plant until it has a self-supporting root system. For the method to work, it is important to wound the section of stem to be buried, either by twisting or cutting it, because it is from the callus that forms over the healing wound that the roots will grow. In theory, you can layer at any time of the year, but because it is an advantage to have new roots growing on the buried portion as soon as possible, mid-spring to late summer is the best time. Speedy rooting ensures that the wound made on the stem before it is buried heals quickly. The benefit of spring layering is that roots will have developed on the buried portion by the fall and the new plant can be moved. Shoots of either the current or previous season's growth root quickest. Older wood will take much longer to form roots and in fact may never do so.

1 *This is the tip of a new cane that has grown from the crown of the plant during the current growing season. It is the natural way for blackberries to spread.*

2 *Scrape out a sloping hole about 3-4in deep, where the shoot tip can reach it. Improve the rooting zone with some peat and grit.*

3 *Lay the shoot in the hole with the actual tip pointing slightly upwards, helped by the sloping hole. Hold the tip in place with a wire loop.*

4 *Scrape soil back over the shoot, holding it in position. Firm down the soil so that there is good contact between the shoot and the soil.*

5 *Push in a cane beside the shoot and tie the two together. This marks where the layering is taking place and also holds the layer firmly.*

Straight layering clematis

1 Gently push a portion of clematis shoot, still attached to the parent plant, into prepared soil. The new plant will grow from the joint.

2 Secure the shoot at the right depth with a wire loop 4-6in long. The shoot will not form roots if it is constantly being moved.

3 Firm the completed layer into place. Mark the site of the layer with a cane so that you do not accidentally hoe up or damage it.

Below: Clematis is far from easy to propagate other than by layering, and even this is not always entirely successful. However, the plants are so attractive that it is well worth trying.

Plants for layering

Akebia, Alnus, Amelanchier, Calluna, Camellia, Carpenteria, Chaenomeles, Chimonanthus, Clematis, Cornus, Corylopsis, Cotinus, Cotoneaster, Daboecia, Daphne, Dianthus, Erica, Eucryphia, Euonymus, Forsythia, Fothergilla, Gaultheria, Hamamelis, Hedera, Hibiscus, Ilex, Jasminum, Juniperus, Kerria, Lavandula, Liquidamber, Lonicera, Magnolia, Mespilus, Morus, Osmanthus, Paeonia suffruticosa, Parrotia, Photinia, Rhododendron, Rubus, Stachyurus, Syringa, Trachelospermum, Vaccinium, Viburnum, Vinca, Vitis, Wisteria.

Layering ivy

Ivy is another climbing/trailing plant that responds well to layering, mainly because it already has root initials along the shoots that will grow out where they make contact with the ground. Ivy is a particularly good plant for growing in poor light conditions or in a spot where it can scramble up into trees and along the ground. The variegated varieties are especially attractive.

Above: Sometimes you find an ivy shoot that has layered itself in the ground. To grow it on, cut it into small sections and pot up each one.

Left: Hedera helix 'Goldheart' is a particularly fine variegated ivy. As with many variegated plants, some new shoots revert to green each year. Pull off the green-leaved shoots as soon as you see them.

Layering winter jasmine

Winter jasmine propagates itself naturally by layering. You have only to look under an established bush and you will see all the young shoots that have produced roots where they touch the ground and become fixed to it. Layering is therefore the method that gardeners should use to propagate this plant.

1 Make a shallow groove in the ground close enough to the winter jasmine plant to guide a young shoot towards it. Lay the shoot in the groove. Have a cane ready for support.

2 Push a thin wire hoop into the ground on either side of the shoot to hold it in place. The hoop need not be very long; it just needs to remain secure in the ground.

3 Cover the shoot with soil, leaving the tip exposed. Secure the shoot tip to the cane. The cane also reminds you of the presence of the layer when you are hoeing.

Above: Winter jasmine in full flower. Although layering is the obvious propagation method, if it is quantity you want, then semi-ripe cuttings root readily in late summer.

4 As the tie will only remain in place for a few months and winter jasmine stems do not expand much in a year, it is safe to use plastic twine. However, twine can bite into the stems of some plants.

Layering a cut section of winter jasmine

This sequence showing a section of stem with side shoots being rooted combines two methods: layering and semi-ripe cuttings.

1 *Take a section of stem with side shoots and lay it in a seed tray or propagator filled with a 50/50 mix of peat and gritty sand. This makes an open, but water-retentive rooting mixture.*

Gritty sand

Peat or substitute

2 *Work the cutting into the rooting mixture with a sawing action, pushing it back and forth and, at the same time, pressing it down.*

3 *When the stem is buried 0.4–0.8in below the surface, firm the mixture lightly so that the shoots are roughly upright. Water the tray well.*

4 *Cover with a lid and place the tray in a shady spot outdoors or under the greenhouse staging. When the stem has produced roots – after about three to four weeks – cut it into pieces and pot them up.*

Natural propagation

Roots readily form on winter jasmine (Jasminum nudiflorum) where any length of young shoot touches the ground. You can take advantage of this natural process of propagation to increase your own stocks of the plant. Simply remove the end section on which the roots are growing and pot it up to make a new plant.

Dropping

Dropping is a form of layering used for propagating multi-stemmed shrubs, such as hebes, hypericum and spiraea, and also bushy ground cover plants, such as heather. It is not suitable for shrubs with stems thicker than about 0.5in, because such stems will take a long time to root – usually well over a year. These respond better either to normal layering or propagation by cuttings. In dropping, the plant is partially buried and roots form on the part of the stems that is underground. Use quite young specimens as subjects for dropping. The system involves very little work and, although it takes quite a long time from start to finish, the only thing you need to do is make sure that the soil in which the "dropped" plant is growing, and that around it, is kept moist. You can also carry out dropping on a young plant growing in a pot, thus increasing your stock before you even plant it. Do not remove the shoots until they have formed roots. As with other forms of layering, rooting usually occurs in a single growing season.

Above: This is Hypericum erectum 'Gemo'. Like many of the shrubby hypericums, it is suitable for dropping because it tends to be clump-forming. Many hypericums can also be propagated by semi-ripe cuttings.

Dropping hypericum

1 To "drop" a potted plant, remove it from its pot. Choose a new pot deep enough to take the plant with much of the stem below the soil.

2 Stand the plant in the bottom of the new pot. Add sowing or cutting mixture or a 50/50 mix of peat and sharp sand so that the lower 3-4in of the stems are covered.

3 Lightly firm down the mix around the stems as you put it in, taking care to exclude all air pockets. If the stems are not in close contact with the mix, they will not root.

4 Continue filling the pot with mixture until the bases of the stems have been buried to the required depth. Allow enough space at the top of the pot for watering.

Dropping thyme

Dropping can be used on young plants already growing in the garden; this is golden thyme. It is important to select young plants for propagation, because the shock of being lifted and handled could kill older specimens. The rooted shoots of plants dropped in mid-spring can be cut off and planted in the following early winter.

1 Dig a hole wide enough for the roots and deep enough to half-bury the stems of the plant.

2 Transfer the plant to the new hole. When digging up the plant from its original position, try to retain a rootball roughly the same size as the spread of the branches. About half the length of the stems should be below ground level.

3 Work in fibrous soil or a seed mix. The old roots sustain the plant while new ones form on buried shoots.

4 Do not bury the plant too deeply or there will be too small an area of leaves exposed to the light. The leaves continue to feed the plant through photosynthesis as roots form on the buried shoots.

5 Once the pot is full enough, shake it quite vigorously so that any loose mix settles around the shoots. Water the container well.

6 Many of the under-ground shoots and shoot bases of this hypericum have roots. If you remove one of the shoots and plant or pot it up separately in spring, it will be able to support itself on these roots.

Grafting

One of the more specialised methods of propagating trees and shrubs is grafting. It involves removing a short length of one-year-old shoot (called a scion) from the plant that you want to propagate and tying it onto the root system of another one. The rootstock, as the root system is called, passes sap and nutrients into the scion, which soon breaks into life and eventually grows into the new plant. Grafting is done in the spring and there are several very important points to bear in mind. First, if the cut surfaces dry out, the chances of success are much reduced. To prevent this, cut the scion first and hold the bottom end in your mouth to keep it moist while making the cut on the rootstock. Second, the two cuts must be totally flat and about the same size so that they can be placed together. Third, at least one edge of the cut on the scion must line up against one edge of the cut on the rootstock. The layer of cells between the bark and the wood must touch, because it is these cells that fuse together. Finally, bind the two portions together without moving the scion, otherwise the fusion will be slower and/or incomplete.

Preparing the scion

1 Using a pencil-thick section of shoot taken from the previous year's growth, remove the thinner top immediately above a bud.

2 Make a slanting cut at the base of the scion, with the lowest bud behind the cut. The finished scion should have three or four buds.

3 Create the tongue of this "whip and tongue" graft by making a shallow, inward and upward cut into the surface of the main cut. Start this smaller cut about a quarter of the way down the main cut.

Suitable plants

Conifers and fruit trees are the most commonly grafted; the method arose mainly because these plants are not easily propagated by other methods, such as cuttings, layering, etc. In the case of fruit trees, the rootstock can be also be used to determine the ultimate vigour and size of the grafted tree. Thus, grafting onto a vigorous rootstock results in a fast-growing and large tree, whereas grafting onto a dwarfing one produces a slow-growing and much smaller tree.

Preparing the rootstock

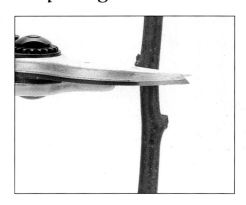

1 Cut off the top of the rootstock, leaving it at least 6-7in long. If it is any shorter, there is a chance that the union (where the scion and the rootstock join) could be buried.

2 The scion and rootstock must fit together precisely. Put them together to see where the lower limit of the cut on the rootstock should be. Make a smooth and flat cut upwards.

3 Make another cut to form the tongue on the rootstock so that the two tongues are opposite each other and fit together. Make sure that all the cuts are smooth and flat.

Completing the graft

1 *The two cuts and tongues match well. The scion should line up with one side of the rootstock, so that the bark on each member is touching.*

2 *The scion will remain in place, held together by the tongues. If the two lots of bark do not correspond exactly, remove a sliver of bark.*

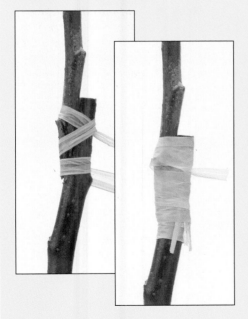

4 *Now the graft is ready for waxing. This excludes the air so that there is no risk of the cut surfaces drying out. Be sure to wax the top of the scion, too.*

3 *Wet some raffia and wind it tightly around the union to hold the cut surfaces together. You could use strips of plastic, but it must not restrict the growth and expansion of the union.*

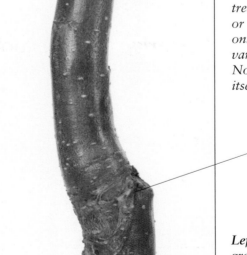

Above: *These apples are produced on trees that are made up of a rootstock, or separately produced set of roots, onto which a scion of the required variety has been budded or grafted. No modern fruit tree will reproduce itself faithfully by seed.*

This is the point at which the scion was grafted or, more likely, budded onto the rootstock. It is called the union.

Left: *The union must never be below ground when the tree is planted, nor must it become covered after planting. If this happens, the scion part of the tree will send out roots that will undo the effect that the rootstock has on the vigour of the tree.*

Part Two

A GARDEN TOUR

Here we take a tour around the garden, examining different groups of plants and how they should be propagated. This section ends with a seasonal guide that will tell you at a glance what plants you should be propagating at any particular time of year. The business of a common propagation thread running through plants of a certain kind really is worth consideration. Plants we treat as annuals and biennials are, for the most part, raised from seed. So are the vast majority of vegetables. They all have to be cheap and easy to grow because they are wanted in relatively large quantities. Seed is, therefore, the easiest way to produce a large number of the same plant. Amongst herbaceous perennials, many are propagated by division. Here the common thread is the way in which plants grow. Many of them are spreading and clump-forming. Those that are not are usually grown from soft basal cuttings taken in spring, although some are grown from seed. There is one important proviso about raising plants from seed. It can only be done where a true breeding line has been established by seedsmen over many years. Plants that do not have this true breeding line can only be reproduced identically by vegetative propagation (cuttings, etc.). Timing of propagation is largely a matter of common sense. For example, soft cuttings are usually available in spring, soon after growth starts. Semi-ripe cuttings come towards the end of the growing season. Hardwood cuttings of shrubs, etc., are fully ripened shoots that have stopped growing and are dormant. Whatever propagation method you use, always allow the new plant time to grow and establish before the following winter. Many are lost by going into their first winter too immature.

Left: A well-stocked garden. **Right:** *Flower variation in hellebores.*

A plant-by-plant guide

The object of this section is to make, if you like, a tour of the garden and, while looking at the different types of plant, see if there is a common method of propagation that runs like a thread through a group. In some cases, such as annuals and biennials, there quite clearly is; virtually all of them are, or can be, grown from seed. However in others, such as ground cover plants, there is such a wide range of plants in the category that very nearly every method of propagation is represented; from cuttings of hypericum and layering ivy to plantlets of bugle (ajuga) and seeds of the perennial sweet pea *(Lathyrus latifolius)*. In most groups, however, there are one or two systems that predominate, such as cuttings for shrubs and division for herbaceous perennials.

Right: A mixed border may feature plants of all types and their propagation methods are equally varied. You can raise the crimson and white lychnis shown here from seed, the lavender from cuttings.

Alpine and rockery plants

Apart from miniature narcissi and other bulb plants, one of the main methods of propagating alpines and rockery plants is from soft cuttings taken in the early summer or even late spring. This is because many true alpines, especially herbaceous types, flower in their natural habitat in the growing period after the snow has melted. Take cuttings when the new growth is about 0.4-0.8in long. Shrubby (woody) true alpines and others suitable for the rockery will often root from semi-ripe cuttings taken in mid- to late summer. The dwarf brooms, and others that set seed readily, often come well from seed. This is best sown soon after it ripens so that it is subjected to a period of cold in winter; otherwise it will not germinate successfully.

Right: This is a great way of displaying alpines: a contrived but natural-looking group in a small corner on a mountainside. Seed is the main method of propagating all these plants other than the conifer.

Alpines and rockery plants

Ajuga	Dianthus
Arabis	Gentiana
Armeria	Helianthemum
Aubretia	Saxifraga
Crassula	Sedum

Left: Gentiana verna is a true alpine, not just a small-growing plant. It can be propagated by soft cuttings, but division and seed are perfectly possible if you want to propagate more than a few plants for the garden.

Annual and biennials

Most annuals and biennials are easily grown from seed – one reason for their popularity as decorative garden plants. Another is that the plants are usually required in large numbers, so an economical method of propagation is essential. A few, such as the Surfinia Series trailing petunias and the succulent sedums and echeverias, are propagated from cuttings and plantlets respectively. Because they flower throughout the summer, annuals are sown either in the fall, for earlier flowering or, more usually, in the spring. Biennials, such as wallflowers, grow in their first year and flower in the spring of the following year, so these are usually sown in late spring or early summer.

Above: Annuals provide a wide palette of flowers for the gardener. Many plants that we treat as annuals are biennial or even perennial.

Above: Honesty (lunaria) is a true biennial. Sow the seed in late spring. Plants grow on vegetatively through summer, fall and winter and start to flower the following spring.

Right: An informal annual border can be grown entirely from seed sown in situ at the same time. Mark out the planting areas with sand in advance.

Annuals and biennials that grow easily from seed

Alyssum	Lunaria
Bellis	Matthiola
Brachyscome	Meconopsis
Calendula	Mimulus
Campanula	Moluccella
Centaurea	Myosotis
Cheiranthus	Nemophila
Chrysanthemum	Nicandra
Clarkia	Nigella
Coreopsis	Oenothera
Digitalis	Pelargonium
Eschscholzia	Polygonum
Godetia	Salvia
Gypsophila	Scabiosa
Helianthus	Silene
Helichrysum	Tropaeolum
Helipterum	Verbena
Hesperis	Viola
Linum	Viscaria
Lobelia	Xeranthemum

Bulbs and corms

Bulbs and corms are almost all propagated either from bulblets or cormlets. After flowering, the parent bulbs of daffodils and narcissi, etc. split up into a number of smaller bulbs. These bulblets grow on and reach individual flowering size after two to four years. A similar system operates with corms, such as crocus and gladioli, except that the new cormlets grow as individuals on the surface of the parent corm, which will have shriveled up by the end of the growing season. Certain bulbous plants, such as anemones and scillas, multiply by seed as well as by splitting. If we include rhizomatous irises here, we find that every season, the main growing section on each rhizome forms two or more new sections. Separate and plant these singly.

Bulbs and corms

Agapanthus	Muscari
Allium	Narcissus
Anemone	Nerine
Chionodoxa	Ornithogalum
Colchicum	Papaver
Crocus	Phacelia
Cyclamen	Rhodohypoxis
Eranthis	Scilla
Eremurus	Sparaxis
Galanthus	Tigridia
Hyacinthus	Tulipa
Iris	Zantedeschia
Leucojum	Zephyranthes
Lilium	

Below: Tulips and narcissi make a superb display, but choose varieties with care to ensure simultaneous flowering. Lift bulbs after flowering. Almost all will have split into smaller bulbs that will not be large enough to flower the following year, but make perfect propagation material.

Climbers

There is such a wide range of climbers that no particular method of propagation dominates. However, the structure of the plants is a clue to the most appropriate system for gardeners, namely one of the several forms of layering. The long and often thin shoots lend themselves ideally to serpentine layering, where the stem is "snaked" on the surface and buried at several leaf joints throughout its length. Roots emerge from the buried node and a shoot, or shoots, appear from the accompanying bud(s). Annual climbers, such as nasturtium and eccremocarpus (Chilean glory vine), grow extremely well from seeds. Chilean glory vine is technically a perennial, but is treated as an annual. One clear exception is wisteria. This should always be grafted onto wisteria seedling rootstocks so that an early flowering plant can be guaranteed. Seedling plants may take many years to flower if, indeed, they ever do.

Above: Grow true passionflower species, such as Passiflora caerulea, from bought or saved seed. Use serpentine layering for outdoor plants.

Left: Most ivies root easily, but you must use a vegetative method, as seeds of named varieties do not come true. Tip cuttings taken during the growing season succeed, as do leaf bud cuttings and layering.

Above: Summer-flowering honey-suckle is one of the most heavily scented and vigorous climbers. Like many plants, it can be propagated by more than one method. If you want several plants, take semi-ripe cuttings in late summer. If you only need one or two plants, layering is fine.

Climbers

Campsis	Lonicera
Clematis	Parthenocissus
Hedera	Passiflora
Humulus	Rubus
Hydrangea	Solanum
petiolaris	Vitis
Jasminum	Wisteria
Lathyrus	

Above: Many of the specie clematis, such as Clematis montana *and* C. tangutica, *grow freely and true from seed, but propagate named varieties, such as 'Nelly Moser' (above) by simple or serpentine layering. Cuttings are difficult.*

Conifers

Traditionally, conifers were grown from heel cuttings taken in mid-spring and mid-fall. Today, grafting onto seedling rootstocks is much more common commercially. This is a far more reliable method than taking cuttings and, because of the huge number of varieties and hybrids that exist today, reliability is crucial. Where a large number of a true specie conifer, such as common juniper (*Juniperus communis*), is wanted for mass planting, and where expense is important, growers normally use seed. However, this does carry the risk of variable seedling plants. In gardens, taking cuttings in mid-spring and mid-fall may still be the most convenient method, because only a small number of plants are wanted.

Conifers

Abies	Larix
Chamaecyparis	Picea
x Cupressocyparis	Pinus
Cupressus	Taxus
Juniperus	Thuja

Above: Conifers are a tricky group of plants to propagate, because there is little or no common thread. The two upright conifers may have been grown from seed or cuttings.

Below: Juniperus *'Blue Carpet' has a procumbent growth habit, which means it is sometimes successfully propagated by layering. This is not possible with upright conifers.*

Fruit

Fruit is something of a mixed bag as regards propagation. Tree fruits, such as apples, pears, plums and cherries, are budded or grafted. This is the most economical way to propagate them and also the most successful; cuttings are unreliable and seeds do not give a true likeness of the parent. In fact, all hybrid varieties of fruit have to be propagated vegetatively. Moving down in plant size, currants (such as redcurrants, blackcurrants and whitecurrants) and gooseberries are grown from hardwood cuttings taken in late fall. Methods for propagating cane fruits, on the other hand, vary. Raise new raspberry canes from suckers, but use tip layering to propagate blackberries and their hybrids, such as tayberries, loganberries, boysenberries and sunberries. Grow strawberries from plantlets that form on the runners.

Fruit

Budding/grafting
Apple
Cherry
Peach/nectarine
Pear
Plum
Quince

Hardwood cuttings
Currants
Fig
Gooseberry
Grape

Plantlets
Strawberry

Simple layering
Blueberry

Tip layering
Blackberry

Suckers
Raspberry

Right: Propagate redcurrants by hardwood cuttings taken in late fall or early winter, as soon as the leaves have dropped. New bushes will be ready for lifting 12 months later.

Below: Apples and other tree fruits are propagated by budding or by grafting small lengths of shoot onto suitable rootstocks that determine the height and growth pattern of the tree.

Grasses, bamboos and allied plants

Although this covers a very large selection of plants, from the enormous pampas grasses, miscanthus and tall bamboos to tiny fescues, nearly all of them can be propagated by division. Most are clump-forming and those that are not, are almost all plants that creep on or below the soil surface and form roots or pop up at varying distances from the parent. Nor must we forget seed; in many grasses seedheads are the main attraction. Ornamental grasses will usually come true from seed because the vast majority are naturally occurring species. You can propagate them by saving seed from your existing plants.

Grasses
Agropyron
Agrostis
Andropogon
Arundinaria
 (bamboo)
Briza
Bromus (bromes)
Carex (sedges)
Cortaderia
Cyperus
Deschampsia
Elymus
Festuca
Holcus
Hystrix
Juncus
Luzula

Melica
Miscanthus
Molinia
Muhlenbergia
Phalaris
Phleum
Phragmites
Poa
Spartina
Stipa
Uncinia

Many of these grasses have a large number of species and cultivars.

Right: The variety of popular ornamental grasses available today is huge and the majority can be successfully propagated by division.

Heaths and heathers

From their appearance, these should come into the ground cover category, but they are really low-growing and small shrubs, rather than naturally creeping plants. This is shown by their reluctance to root when they make contact with the ground. This alone makes them poor subjects for ground cover. As they are more shrubby than creeping, propagate them in late summer as shrubs, from heel cuttings of the current year's shoots. They can also be layered, but this is a long job and not very satisfactory.

Heaths and heathers
Calluna
Daboecia
Erica

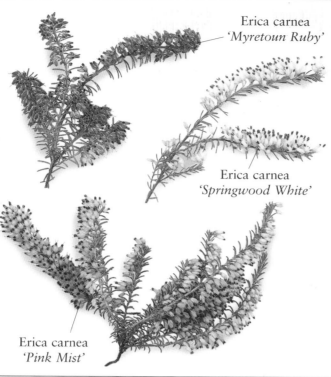

Erica carnea 'Myretoun Ruby'

Erica carnea 'Springwood White'

Erica carnea 'Pink Mist'

Right: *When heaths and heathers form part of a wider display, you need a good succession of plants. Once they start to deteriorate, replace them. The cheapest way of doing this is to grow your own.*

Left: *Being woody by nature, layering or dropping are not as good a method of propagating heathers as it might seem. Nor are they long-lived plants. Propagate them regularly by semi-ripe cuttings.*

Ground cover plants

A huge number of species are suitable as ground cover, but most have one important thing in common: they are low-growing or spreading, and many actually run along the ground. Once again, the habit of the plant is often a clue to the best way to propagate it. For woody ground cover plants, such as *Cotoneaster horizontalis*, layering is excellent if you want to make the most of each plant. However, semi-ripe cuttings in late summer will yield a large number of young plants, as they root very easily. Herbaceous creeping plants, such as ajuga, perpetuate themselves without any help; plantlets or creeping stems root wherever they touch the ground. Always bear one important factor in mind: choose ground cover plants with care. You will need plenty of them for quick and effective results, so they must be easy to propagate at home or once planted. Hypericum and periwinkle are good choices from this point of view.

Ground cover plants

Acaena	Gaultheria	
Ajuga	Genista	
Alchemilla	Geranium	
Artemisia	Hebe	
Aubretia	Hedera	
Bergenia	Helianthemum	
Bilberry	Helleborus	Physalis
Brooms	Hypericum	Polygonum
Cerastium	Iberis	Potentilla
Ceratostigma	Juniperus	Rhododendron
Chamaemelum	Lamium	(dwarf)
Clematis	Lathyrus	Rosa
Cotoneaster	latifolia	Santolina
Cytisus	Mahonia	Sarcococca
Dianthus	Mint	Senecio
Doronicum	Nepeta	Symphytum
Epimedium	Pachysandra	Thymus
Ferns	Phlomis	Vinca

Below: *Shrubby hypericums make good, but shortlived, low-growing shrubs. Take semi-ripe cuttings in summer or keep small specimens for propagation as hardwood cuttings or for dropping.*

Hedges

Hedging and ground cover plants fall into much the same sort of category in that you are likely to be using them in relatively large numbers. For that reason, they must be quick and easy to propagate or cheap to buy. By far the most economical hedging plants can be raised from seed, the cheapest method of all. Do not sow them where the hedge is to run, but in nursery rows and then transplant the seedlings at the end of their first growing season. Hawthorn and beech will propagate readily from seed. Hardwood cuttings are also very economical, but unfortunately only a limited number of plants can be propagated successfully in this way. Roses, privet and *Lonicera nitida* are the most successful. The best way with hardwood cuttings is to prepare the ground along which the hedge is to run and then insert the cuttings in a double, staggered line. This means that a good "take" is essential or you will be forever removing the dead cuttings and replacing them with new.

Below: Ornamental shrubs may not be an obvious choice for hedges, but they are cheap and easy to propagate. Raise shrubby potentillas from semi-ripe cuttings, Rosa rugosa *from seed.*

Potentilla fruticosa 'Abbotswood'

Hedges

Buxus	Ilex
Carpinus	Ligustrum
Crataegus	Lonicera nitida
Cytisus	Potentilla
Fagus	Taxus

Left: This is a trial of various hedging plants at Wisley. The best way of propagating many common hedging plants, such as beech, box and yew, is by hardwood cuttings. Earth them up for the winter and unearth them a year later. By then, the buried shoots will have rooted.

Herbs

These can be broadly divided into woody, herbaceous and annual plants. As with other groups, the woody ones are usually best propagated from semi-ripe cuttings taken in late summer. This would cover such subjects as hyssop, sage, rosemary, thyme and lavender. Many herbaceous herbs, such as tarragon and all the mints, can be divided very easily in late fall or early spring. Clumps of the bulbous chives should be split up every few years to keep them young and productive. However, any of the herb genera are best grown from seed annually. The yearling plants usually give the best growths for immediate use or for drying and later use. Even perennials such as fennel and rue respond best to annual sowing so that they do not become old and woody, tall, coarse and sparse. Parsley (a biennial herb) must be sown *in situ* (where it is to grow) every spring; transplanting encourages bolting.

Above: No one propagation method can be applied to the majority of herbs. They are fairly evenly divided between seed, division and semi-ripe cuttings.

Herbs

Laurus	Origanum
Lavandula	Rosmarinus
Mentha	Salvia
Nepeta	Thymus

Below: A few herbs, such as chives, grow from bulbs. Lift them in winter, split the clump into sections with about 12 bulbs in each and replant each one where it is to grow.

Perennials

You are most likely to see these in mixed ornamental borders where there is a selection of shrubs, annuals, biennials, bulbs and, of course, herbaceous plants (another name for perennials). With few exceptions, the normal way of propagating perennials is by splitting up overgrown clumps (division) to keep them young and full of flowers. However, some, such as delphiniums, do not split readily, so soft cuttings in the spring are the best way of increasing them. Lupins are another exception. On limy, chalky soils they are very shortlived and are usually best treated as biennials or even annuals. Sow seed early every summer and throw the finished plants out after just one flowering. (In fact, where named varieties are not involved, you can raise quite a few herbaceous perennials from seed.) Grow named varieties of lupins from soft cuttings in the spring.

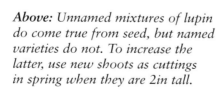

Above: Unnamed mixtures of lupin do come true from seed, but named varieties do not. To increase the latter, use new shoots as cuttings in spring when they are 2in tall.

Left: Wild and old species of cranesbill (Geranium) come true from seed. Increase new ones and all F1 hybrids by division or root cuttings.

Right: Divide asters in the fall or spring before the clumps become small-flowered and woody. Dig them up, split them and throw away the old center of the clump.

Left: Tall helianthus, such as this 'Lemon Queen', are easily propagated in several ways. Division in fall is the simplest method, or take basal cuttings in spring. Alternatively, you may prefer to sow seed in spring. The clumps will need renewing every three to four years to keep them vigorous.

Perennials

Acanthus	Lobelia
Achillea	Lupinus
Alstroemeria	Lychnis
Alyssum	Malva
Aquilegia	Monarda
Arundinaria	Osmunda
Aster	Oxalis
Astilbe	Paeonia
Bergenia	Papaver
Caltha	Penstemon
Campanula	Phlox
Carex	Phormium
Chrysanthemum	Phygelius
Cortaderia	Physalis
Crocosmia	Platycodon
Delphinium	Polemonium
Dianthus	Polygonatum
Dicentra	Primula
Doronicum	Prunella
Echinops	Pulmonaria
Erigeron	Pulsatilla
Eryngium	Pyrethrum
Euphorbia	Rheum
Gaillardia	Romneya
Gentiana	Rudbeckia
Geranium	Salvia
Geum	Scabiosa
Gypsophila	Sedum
Helenium	Sisyrinchium
Helleborus	Solidago
Hemerocallis	Teucrium
Hosta	Thalictrum
Incarvillea	Tolmiea
Inula	Tradescantia
Iris	Trillium
Juncus	Verbascum
Kniphofia	Veronica
Lamium	Vinca
Liatris	

Roses

When gardeners think of propagating roses, it is usually hybrid teas and floribundas that spring to mind. Almost without exception, these must be raised by budding the required variety onto a seedling rootstock, a specialised task but one that can be learned with practice. A few can be raised from hardwood cuttings taken in early winter but the percentage "take" is usually very low, depending on the variety. Much the same goes for climbers, but ramblers can be grown successfully on their own roots, so hardwood cuttings will give good results. If you want just one plant from a rambler, take about six cuttings to be on the safe side. Hybrid and named varieties of shrub roses also need to be budded because vegetative propagation is the only way of reproducing them true to type. However, most of the true specie roses, such as *Rosa rugosa*, *rubrifolia* and *moyesii*, will grow very well from seed, which is readily available from their ornamental hips.

Roses

Climbers	Patio roses
Floribundas	Ramblers
Hybrid teas	Shrub roses
Miniatures	Specie roses

Above: To increase Rosa rugosa, gather the ripe hips in fall, break them up and mix them with sand. Keep them outdoors in a container until spring and then sow them.

Above: Propagate the new patio roses, such as this 'Sweet Dream', by budding so that they come true to type. Hardwood cuttings occasionally take root, so it is always worth trying.

Left: All bedding roses – the ones grown for mass displays of color – are propagated by budding the desired varieties onto Rosa laxa rootstocks. Some varieties will grow from hardwood cuttings taken in late fall, so it is always worth having a try.

Above: 'Scarlet Fire', a spectacular shrub rose with attractive hips, does not come true to the seeds they contain. Propagate it by budding.

Shrubs

This group includes an enormous range of woody plants so it will not surprise you to learn that all methods of propagation are applicable. However, the one that will be successful in virtually all cases is common layering. Its other advantage is that it can be carried out at any time of the year, because you are not actually using a piece of vegetation removed from the plant. It is also a very easy method of propagation. However, it is also very slow because you should not sever the rooted layer until a full growing season after it has been layered. Another almost universally successful method of propagating shrubs, at least deciduous ones, is to take semi-ripe cuttings in late summer. It is often said that, when in doubt, this is the time you are most likely to succeed with cuttings.

Many shrubs can be grown from seed but, as always, hybrids and most named varieties will not come true. However, that should not stop you trying; raising new varieties from seed can be most interesting and even rewarding.

Right: Most shrubs are increased by semi-ripe cuttings, but propagate the butterfly bush, Buddleia davidii, *by softwood cuttings in spring or hardwood cuttings in late fall.*

Right: Strike fuchsias from softwood cuttings taken as early as possible in the growing season. They can be as little as 0.4in long. Remove any flower buds. Pot the cuttings in a peat mix and put in a plastic bag to root.

Below: Take leaf bud or semi-ripe cuttings of camellia in late summer, or layer this lovely shrub in spring or summer. Use an acidic potting mix.

'Candidissima'

'Reg Ragland'

'Furo-an'

'Blaze of Glory'

Shrubs (flowering and foliage)	
Abelia	Lavatera
Amelanchier	Leycesteria
Aucuba	Ligustrum
Berberis	Magnolia
Buddleia	Mahonia
Buxus	Olearia
Camellia	Osmanthus
Carpinus	Philadelphus
Ceanothus	Phlomis
Chaenomeles	Photinia
Chimonanthus	Pieris
Choisya	Piptanthus
Cistus	Pittosporum
Cornus	Poncirus
Cotinus	Potentilla
Cotoneaster	Pyracantha
Crataegus	Rhododendron
Cytisus	Rhus
Daphne	Ribes
Deutzia	Salix
Diervilla	Sambucus
Elaeagnus	Santolina
Escallonia	Senecio
Fatsia	Spartium
Forsythia	Spiraea
Fuchsia	Symphoricarpos
Garrya	Syringa
Gaultheria	Tamarix
Genista	Ulex
Hamamelis	Viburnum
Hebe	Vinca
Hedera	Weigela
Hydrangea	Yucca
Hypericum	Zauschneria
Kerria	

Right: Hydrangea maculata *takes very easily from semi-ripe cuttings. If you have a greenhouse or an electric propagator, take them in mid- or late summer. They will also root readily outdoors under a cloche if taken in late summer or early fall.*

Trees

Much of what has been said about propagating shrubs also applies to trees. However, whereas layering and semi-ripe cuttings are the most popular methods for shrubs, budding or grafting and seed are more often used for trees. Common layering is largely impossible with trees; they have to be air layered, which is not an easy task. Nor are cuttings always suitable; hardwood cuttings, in particular, often produce plants with kinked stems. This does not matter with a shrub, which is going to have several stems in any case, but it is not a good start for a shapely tree. Unless you wish to try, or you are already adept at, budding or grafting, it is better to buy trees than to try to propagate them at home by vegetative means. Growing trees from seed is a different matter; chestnuts, sycamore, ash, etc., are the most likely to succeed, but do not let this deter you from trying others.

Above: *In common with all sycamores that bear ornamental foliage, Acer platanoides 'Drummondii' must be grafted onto sycamore seedlings if they are to be reproduced faithfully. Growing from seed always results in common sycamore seedlings.*

Above: *Budding or grafting crab apples onto the same rootstocks as fruiting apples produces trees true to type and of a predetermined vigor, according to the rootstock.*

Left: *Being a true species, the strawberry tree will come true from seed, but takes longer to make a tree than if grown from semi-ripe cuttings taken in late summer or early fall.*

Trees

Acer	Laburnum
Aesculus	Malus
Betula	Platanus
Catalpa	Prunus
Cercis	Pyrus
Cornus	Quercus
Eucalyptus	Salix
Fagus	Sorbus
Fraxinus	Syringa
Ilex	

Vegetables

You should not be surprised to find vegetables included in a book about propagation; they are simply plants with a different purpose in the garden, edible rather than decorative. As with ornamental plants that are required in large numbers (e.g. for hedges or ground cover), nearly all popular vegetables are grown from seed. This is also because almost no vegetables remain in the ground for more than a year; the vast majority for a good deal less. It is therefore easier to look at the main exceptions to those raised from seed; in other words, those raised vegetatively. The obvious crop is potatoes, which are grown at home by planting medium-sized, or seed, tubers in the spring. Jerusalem artichokes are another vegetable grown from tubers. The point about both is that seed-raised plants give very variable and usually inferior results. Asparagus is another that should be grown from bought plants.

Several vegetables are grown by planting small bulbs; shallots, garlic and onions from sets are examples. However, onions are also grown from seed. Some people have been known to grow runner beans from the previous year's saved plants, but these do not compare well with those grown from seed.

Vegetables

Division	Celeriac	Spinach
Asparagus	Celery	Sweetcorn
	Chard	Tomato
Root cuttings	Chicory	Turnip
Sea kale	Cucumber	
	Leek	*Small bulbs*
Rooted suckers	Lettuce	Onion, shallot,
Globe artichoke	Marrow,	garlic
	zucchini, etc.	
Seed	Onion, shallot,	*Tubers*
Beans	garlic	Jerusalem artichoke
Beetroot	Parsnip	Potato
Brassicas	Peas	
Carrot	Radish	

Right: Radishes are quick and easy to grow from seed sown in situ *throughout the growing season.*

Water plants

Although there are not many true water plants, there are several different genera, so a variety of propagation methods is possible. The one that features least widely is probably seed sowing. On the other hand, division probably heads the list. This would apply to most of the reeds and rushes, together with water lilies. However, there is no clear leader or one system that lends itself to a good range of plants. The safest plan is to examine the structure and appearance of any specific plant and use this to determine the most appropriate method of propagating it. That, or buy a new plant!

Popular water plants
Aponogeton distachyos
  (water hawthorn)
Butomus umbellatus
  (flowering rush)
Calla palustris (bog arum)
Iris laevigata
Iris pseudacorus (yellow flag iris)
Nymphaea (water lily)
Sagittaria sagittifolia
  (common arrowhead)
Scirpus 'Zebrinus' (zebra rush)
Stratiotes aloides (water soldier)

Right: Most water plants, such as this 'Conqueror' water lily, divide easily, and the divisions can be grown in pots standing in trays of water until they are large enough to be planted in the pool. This often happens in the same growing season.

A seasonal guide

The object of this seasonal guide is to summarize the different methods of plant propagation and determine when to apply each one. That immediately poses a problem, because there is nearly always latitude with jobs in the garden, and when to propagate plants is no exception. You might also look at things the other way round and say, "it is now early spring, so what propagation methods and subjects are appropriate at this time of year?" Remember that many propagation methods are only possible at specific times of the year. For example, softwood cuttings are only taken during the spring, whereas division is a job for when plants are dormant, or nearly so.

As we have seen, the way that plants behave in the wild will give you a clue as to how and when to propagate them yourself. Climbers, for example, are often propagated by layering, either in the simplest form or by tip layering or even serpentine layering. But first, a word about seed sowing, because you will not find it mentioned a great deal in this section. The main reason for this is that seed sowing can take place all year round, depending on what you are sowing and the necessary conditions for success. For example, bedding plants and most summer vegetables are sown in early or mid-spring, but some are sown in heat in a greenhouse, whereas others can be sown outside where they are to mature. You must also consider how appropriate it is to propagate a given plant by seed. Many modern hybrids, for example, do not come true when grown from seed.

Anemone *x* hybrida *'Honorine Jobert' (white).* A. hupehensis *'Prinz Heinrich' (pink)*

WINTER

This is very much the season for propagating dormant plants by division. (In fact, two of the biggest tasks associated with plants – digging them up and planting them – are best carried out when they are dormant.) Division is possibly the simplest of all propagation methods. It simply involves digging up dormant herbaceous plants, such as asters, solidago and herbaceous phlox, splitting them up into a number of smaller portions and replanting each one. Taking root cuttings of plants such as peony, sea kale and, again, herbaceous phlox, is related to division and also a job for the winter. When taking root cuttings, look for adventitious buds on the root. When it is parted from the parent plant, these buds will send out the new shoots.

Early winter is the best time to take hardwood cuttings, just after the leaves have dropped. This gives the cuttings all winter in which to form a callus on the buried end from which roots will grow in the spring. A hardwood cutting is usually about 6in long but, when propagating vines, you only need a single bud with a short length of stem. Vines root easily, so long cuttings are not needed.

Below: *Lift perennials (here marjoram) in late fall and divide small clumps by hand. Older ones may need more force.*

Above: *Take hardwood cuttings in winter. Roses (above) do not always "take," but you seldom need many and it is so easy to do.*

SPRING

Spring is when perennial plants start to grow again after their winter rest and seeds begin to germinate to give rise to another generation of annuals. Annuals are all the plants that germinate, grow, flower, seed and die in a single growing season. They include both ornamental plants and vegetables. You can sow half-hardy annuals under cover, but wait until the risk of spring frosts is over before sowing or planting them outside. Hardy annuals will withstand the frost, so they can be sown outside from early spring.

A good reason for propagating in spring is that the resulting plants have a complete growing season in which to root, establish and grow on, thus ensuring strong and sizeable plants before the onset of their first winter.

Early and mid-spring are good times to carry out grafting, once the sap is moving and growth has started. When grafting deciduous woody

plants, such as fruit trees, the scion (the piece that is cut from one plant and grafted on to another) should still be dormant, without any signs of growth. You can help plants stay dormant by heeling them into the ground at the base of a shady wall or some similar sunless place.

Early spring is a good time to dig up any suckers from around

Below: To sow a patch of mixed hardy annuals, first pour out the seeds into individual heaps. Mix some of each of the seeds with the sand and scatter this over the allotted area. Rake in and water if necessary.

Above: Sowing annuals in spring where they are to flower saves time and work, and the plants flower sooner. Make sure that you choose hardy annuals; half-hardies would be killed by the frost.

Simple layering

Layering can start in spring; no roots will form until the soil temperature rises. Obvious plants for layering are those with lower branches close to the ground and climbers whose stems can easily be brought down to ground level.

1 To layer a clematis (above), make a shallow channel close to the parent plant. Lay down a shoot from the previous year's growth and secure it at a leaf node with a wire hoop pressed into the soil.

2 Cover the stem section by filling the channel with soil. Firm it down and mark the buried section with a stone or two. These act as a reminder that the layer is there and also help to secure it in the ground.

appropriate trees and shrubs and plant them either where they are to stay or in nursery rows in the vegetable plot. It is best if they are still dormant, but even if there are the first signs of growth, such as buds bursting, results should be acceptable. Depending on the parent plant, suckers may or may not already have roots.

You can continue to divide herbaceous plants during the spring until the shoots are 1in or so high. And you can root offsets in spring. Although rooting offsets is not really akin to division, it does involve a

partially formed plant. In this case, the plant is at the end of a short stalk, as in sempervivums.

You can propagate lilies during the spring by pushing individual scales into pots of sowing mixture.

Although you can start taking softwood cuttings in mid-spring, it is better to wait until late spring, when they will be bigger and more likely to root. Most of them will be taken from ornamental shrubs.

If you did not manage to divide herbaceous plants earlier, many can be propagated in mid- or late spring by taking soft, basal cuttings. They root quite easily in a peat/sand mix.

Most forms of layering can start in mid-spring. This includes simple layering, when the center of a section of shoot is buried to encourage roots to form on the underground part. Mid-spring is the time for air layering and also serpentine layering. The latter involves burying several parts of a long shoot, such as ivy. It is one of the most economical kinds of layering. Young shrubs with many shoots originating from near the ground can be "drop layered" or "dropped" in mid-spring. By fall they will have rooted, so cut off the rooted shoots and plant them up in early winter.

Right: The best way to raise plants with large seeds, such as sweet peas or lupins, is to sow them singly into pots or modular trays. Be sure to water them regularly. When the pots are filled with root, plant out the seedlings.

Left: Sweetcorn seedlings hate to be disturbed. A good way to sow them is individually in deep "tube" pots. You can make your own from toilet paper rolls. Fill them with seed mix or multi-purpose potting mix and support them in trays. After about a month, when there is no longer any risk of frost, plant them out, in their tubes (which will biodegrade) about 18in apart.

Right: Many sweet-corn varieties do well outdoors in temperate climates. All are grown from seed. They differ in their degree of sweetness. Do not grow "supersweet" varieties amongst standard ones.

Lupin cuttings

Several herbaceous plants, such as lupins (below) and delphiniums, cannot be increased by division because of their structure. Propagate named varieties vegetatively so that they remain true to type. Take cuttings in spring and keep them in a greenhouse, propagator or at a sunny window.

1 *Once growth has started, use any healthy new shoots that appear at the base of the plant as cuttings. Cut them off cleanly. They should be 1-2in long.*

2 *Using a sharp knife, carefully remove any torn ends and brown leaf debris, leaving a green, smooth, healthy cutting.*

3 *Dip the base in hormone rooting powder and push it into a 3-3.5in pot filled with a 50/50 peat and sharp sand mix or a cuttings mix. Water and place in a large plastic bag. Secure the top.*

SUMMER

Summer is the period of greatest activity for plant propagation, and most of the methods described can be applied throughout the season. It is not until late summer, when many plants have stopped growing for the year, that some systems become inappropriate and others take over. By midsummer, for example, semi-ripe cuttings should be replacing softwood cuttings. Semi-ripe cuttings can be taken right up until the early fall, by which time they are becoming ripe and firm and almost hardwood cuttings. If you are in doubt as to the best way of propagating a particular shrub, then semi-ripe cuttings taken from midsummer to early fall are likely to be the most successful. However, at the very beginning of the summer, you can still succeed with soft basal cuttings of late-starting herbaceous plants. Some varieties of asters come into this category.

A job for early summer, straight after flowering, is splitting up rhizomatous irises. These are the ones with fleshy "tubers" that lie on the soil surface. Replant just the end section, the one with the fan of leaves.

Simple, serpentine and air layering are all successful throughout the summer, but do not forget that it is always better to propagate a plant early in the growing season so that it has the maximum time in which to root, become established and grow.

You can propagate blackberries, both fruiting and ornamental, by tip layering the current season's new shoots during mid- and late summer. If you want more than just one or two plants, cut the current season's canes into leaf bud cuttings at any time during the same period.

Propagate border carnations and pinks during mid- and late summer by taking pipings (the special name for the cuttings) or by layering them – you can layer them and simply leave them in place in the border. The plants age very quickly and this keeps young plants coming.

Another form of layering is found among the few plants that have plantlets on the end of runners, such as strawberries. Propagate these by pegging down the plantlets in mid- and late summer. The half-hardy tolmiea carries its plantlets on the edges of mature leaves. Simply take these off during the summer and pot them up.

Lift daffodils, narcissi, crocus and many other spring-flowering bulbs and corms in summer after the foliage has died down. The original bulbs and corms will have split up into several new ones – just clean them and keep them dry until you plant them again in the fall. They will take two to three years to flower.

You can still increase lilies and similar bulbs by planting up the bulb scales during this period of the year.

Tolmiea plantlets

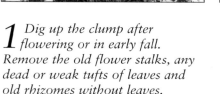

1 Tolmiea menziesii *produces little plants on the part of the leaf where it joins the leaf stalk. In the wild, these drop off and root. To propagate them, cut off the whole leaf.*

Dividing bearded irises

The structure of irises varies between bulbs (Dutch iris), stolons (Iris japonica) and rhizomes (bearded iris). Divide clusters of bearded iris into smaller plants every two to three years to improve the flowering.

1 *Dig up the clump after flowering or in early fall. Remove the old flower stalks, any dead or weak tufts of leaves and old rhizomes without leaves.*

2 *Cut back the leaves to reduce transpiration and replant what is left. Bury the roots but leave the rhizomes on the surface. Water the plant thoroughly to settle the soil.*

2 *Retain 0.5-1in of leaf stalk and push it into a cuttings mixture in a tray or pot. Make sure that the plantlet is in touch with the mix and it will soon send down roots.*

Take whole leaf cuttings of succulent-leaved herbaceous plants, such as sedum, in early and midsummer. They take very easily and are botanically the same as lily bulb scales.

The one summer job that remains is budding, or "bud grafting," to give it its proper name. You can do this all through the summer and, although fruit trees and roses are the normal subjects, it is now used to propagate a wide range of trees and shrubs. Once mastered, bud grafting is a quick and successful method of propagation.

Lavender cuttings

Lavender is an easy subject for propagation. Semi-ripe cuttings taken in mid- to late summer root very easily. After just one year the new bushes can be planted in their final positions.

1 *To propagate lavender, buy a bushy potted plant with few flower stems from a garden center in mid- to late summer. Cut off semi-ripe shoots.*

2 *Dip the base of each cutting in hormone rooting powder and push it into a cuttings mix. Stand the pot in a shady greenhouse or at a window.*

Right: *Very few gardens are complete without their lavender bush or even a hedge. On a still and sunny summer evening, their scent is out of this world. This is French lavender, Lavandula stoechas.*

FALL

Fall is far from a dull time in the plant propagation calendar. The first half is a good time to finish those tasks you did not get done earlier; for example, although it is certainly getting late, you can still bud your roses. However, late fall is a good time to start taking hardwood cuttings from shrubs – including specie roses and other kinds that do not need to be budded. The usual sign that the time is right to take hardwood cuttings is when the leaves have dropped. It is even possible to take semi-ripe cuttings until late mid-

Below: *It is worth taking a close look at a foxglove to appreciate just how delicate and exotic-looking it is. This lovely biennial deserves to be more widespread.*

Above: *Lift gladioli corms when the flowers are over. Collect and dry the cormlets around the base of the parent for spring sowing.*

fall, but success cannot be guaranteed. However, cormlets are really in season. These are the little growths that cluster around the base of gladiolus corms. Collect these when you lift the corms if you want to increase your stock of a certain variety. And that brings us back to the division of herbaceous plants – the point at which we started.

Below: *You can save more than enough seed from one stem of a foxglove plant. Sow the seeds in late spring or early summer for flowering a year later.*

Once established, you will have a constant supply of seed.

Propagation diary

The table below shows the type of propagation that can be done at each time of year, although local weather conditions may alter the timing to some degree. An asterisk * denotes the best season for each method. Where no * is present, the method is still possible, but the results may not be as good. Most of the propagation methods mentioned below are described throughout the book. Seeds of one kind or another can be sown more or less throughout the year, depending on what they are and the facilities you have available.

Early spring
* Division
* Suckers, rooted and unrooted
Bulb scales
Grafting
Offsets
Root cuttings

Mid-spring
* Bulb scales
* Division
* Grafting

* Dropping (drop layering)
* Simple, serpentine and air layering
* Soft basal cuttings
Offsets
Softwood cuttings

Late spring
* Bulb scales
* Simple, serpentine and air layering
* Soft basal cuttings
* Softwood cuttings

Early summer
* Budding
* Bulb scales
* Leaf bud cuttings
* Plantlets on leaves
* Splitting up rhizomatous irises
* Runners
* Simple, serpentine and air layering
* Softwood cuttings
* Succulent leaf cuttings
Bulblets
Semi-ripe cuttings
Soft basal cuttings

Midsummer
* Budding
* Bulb scales
* Leaf bud cuttings
* Pipings and layering
* Plantlets on leaves
* Runners
* Semi-ripe cuttings
* Simple, serpentine and air layering
* Succulent leaf cuttings
* Tip layering (rubus)
Bulblets
Cormlets
Softwood cuttings

Left: The spring is a busy time in the garden, when a wide range of overwintered plants, such as these ivies and primroses, are moved into larger pots for the new season.

Late summer
* Budding
* Leaf bud cuttings (rubus)
* Pipings and layering
* Semi-ripe cuttings
* Simple, serpentine and air layering
* Tip layering (rubus)
Bulb scales

Early fall
* Cormlets
* Semi-ripe cuttings
Budding

Mid-fall
Semi-ripe cuttings

Above: The vibrant tones of Japanese acers bring welcome color to the fall garden. Japanese acers are normally propagated by grafting the required variety onto, for example, an Acer palmatum seedling.

Late fall
* Division
* Hardwood cuttings

Early winter
* Division
* Hardwood cuttings including vines
* Root cuttings

Index to Plants

Credits

The majority of the photographs featured in this book have been taken by Neil Sutherland and are © Quadrillion Publishing Ltd. The publishers wish to thank the following photographers for providing additional photographs, credited here by page number and position on the page, i.e. (B)Bottom, (T)Top, (C)Center, (BL)Bottom left, etc.

Peter Blackburne-Maze: 59(BR)
Eric Crichton: 12(T), 22(TR), 36(TR), 37(BR), 47(TR), 51(TR), 53(BL), 55(BC,BR), 61(TL,BR), 64(TR), 67(CL), 69(TR), 70, 73(BR), 74(TR), 75(TR,BL), 76(BR), 77(TR), 81(C), 88(TR)
John Glover: Copyright page, 15(TR,C), 29(BR), 34(TR), 43(BL), 47(CR), 48(TC), 62(TL), 72(BL), 73(CL), 78(BL), 79(BR), 82(TR), 88(BL), 89(TR,BL)
Garden Picture Library: 33(R, Bob Challinor)
Harpur Garden Library: 18(T, Peter Wooster, USA)
S & O Mathews: Half-title page, 10, 12(CTL), 13(C), 32(C), 36(BR), 41(TR), 42(TR), 48(BL), 58(BR), 60(BL), 63(BL), 78(BR), 79(CL), 80(TC,BL,BR), 82(BL), 83(BR), 85(C)
Clive Nichols Garden Pictures: 45(BL), 56(BL, Designer Elisabeth Woodhouse), 72(TR, Glazeley Old Rectory, Shropshire), 74(BL, Clive Nichols/Mainau, Lake Constance), 81(BR)
Geoffrey Rogers: 12(BL), 23(TL), 25(BL,C), 35(BR), 72(BR), 75(BR), 79(TR,BL), 80(TR), 81(TC), 84(BL)

Acknowledgments

The publishers would like to thank the following people and organizations for their help during the preparation of this book:

M. H. Berlyn Co. Ltd.; Burton McCall Ltd.; Coblands Herbaceous Unit, Ivy Hatch, Kent; June Crow at Rose Cottage, Hartley, Kent; Peter Jackson of Scotsdales Garden Centre, Cambridge; Merriments, Hurst Green, East Sussex; Murrells Nursery, Pulborough, West Sussex; Andrew Norfield Seeds, St. Briavels, Goucestershire; R. V. Roger Ltd., Nurserymen, Pickering, North Yorkshire.